FROM TENSION
TO RELAXATION

M. W. SULLIVAN

**GRANGER-DOYLE
3280 ALPINE ROAD
MENLO PARK, CALIFORNIA**

FROM TENSION TO RELAXATION

M. W. SULLIVAN

ABOUT THE AUTHOR...In addition to his doctorate, M. W. Sullivan has two master's degrees and two bachelor's degrees. He has taught at the Choate School, the University of Puerto Rico, the University of Madrid, Yale University, Marquette University, and Hollins College.

Dr. Sullivan was one of the principal investigators for a Carnegie Corporation grant in automated teaching media. He has also directed two institutes under the National Defense Education Act.

The author of three books, seven programmed courses and numerous other publications, Dr. Sullivan is now president of a research organization devoted to the preparation of programmed materials.

TABLE OF CONTENTS

Page

TABLE OF CONTENTS

Page

TABLE OF CONTENTS

TABLE OF CONTENTS

Page

TO THE READER. . .

FROM TENSION TO RELAXATION is designed for the many people who wish to live more relaxed, happier lives. The programmed form of the course encourages you to participate in a consciously directed process of relaxation.

This book has the following objectives:

(1) To make you more relaxed and comfortable with yourself and your associates.

(2) To help you lead a longer and healthier life.

(3) To teach you to fall asleep quickly and to sleep soundly.

(4) To prevent you from worrying.

(5) To increase your efficiency at work.

(6) To teach you to rid yourself of feelings of tension, rage, fear, hatred, guilt and inadequacy.

(7) To help you to be happier and to contribute to the happiness of others.

It is not necessary to write in this book. Simply say each answer to yourself, and then check it by pulling down your slider.

The study of this course has given many readers a new control over themselves and their lives. The contents of an ordinary book seldom become an intimate part of you. In this program, however, you will interact constantly with the information presented; the things you learn will enter into your reaction patterns, and a relaxed attitude will soon become part of your normal behavior.

On the next page are some sample frames, designed to help you use this book. Cover the answers on the right with your slider.

SAMPLE FRAMES

All answers in this course are oral.

When you reach a blank like the one at the
end of this sentence, you will give an oral
_____.   answer
  (Give your answer; then pull your slider
  down and check.)

The title of this book is FROM _____   TENSION
TO RELAXATION.

This - is/isn't - a programmed course in   is
relaxation. (Choose the correct word.)

Must you write your answers in this book?   no

When you are given a series of choices like
the following, you will select

  1. the wrong answer.

  2. no answer.

  3. the correct answer.   3

Often you will be asked a question which calls
for your opinion. We will give an answer
representative of the responses of the people
who helped develop this course.

Your answer to such a question may differ
from ours. Does this mean that your answer
is necessarily wrong?   no

Always say your answer to yourself
- before/after - you pull the slider down   before
to check.

Before looking at the next page, you will cover
the answer column with your _____.   slider

Now turn to page 1, cover the answers with your
slider, and begin studying FROM TENSION TO
_____.   RELAXATION

AN INITIAL DEFINITION

Relaxation may be defined in many ways. For
the purposes of this course, we will define it
as the absence of tension. Thus we will say
that a person who is not tense is _____.   relaxed

As you take this program, you will define
relaxation more and more precisely. For
the moment you can best appreciate your
need for relaxation by seeing how its
opposite, _____, affects the lives of   tension
average people in the course of a normal
day.

WAKING UP

Barry Stone knows that he has been getting
too little sleep. He goes to bed early, but
he is so worried about problems at the
office that sleep eludes him.

After tossing and turning until 1 a.m., Barry
finally takes two sleeping pills. Toward the
end of another restless half-hour, the pills
take effect and Barry sleeps until 7.

Barry has spent - a pleasant/an unpleasant -   an unpleasant
night.

He has difficulty in going to sleep. Does he
seem able to resolve this difficulty himself,   He has to rely
or does he have to rely on drugs?   on drugs.

Upon awakening, Barry is still plagued by the
same problems, but they are now somewhat
obscured by his usual early-morning fog.
Even after two cups of coffee, he still feels
groggy from the effects of the sleeping pills.

It takes Barry so long to get going that he has
to gulp down his breakfast while dressing. He
then swallows a pill designed to prevent
indigestion and hurries out to his car. A glance
at his watch tells him that he is ten minutes
behind schedule.

Without knowing anything further about Barry
Stone, we would tend to describe his mood
this morning as

1. ecstatically happy.

2. tired and harried.

3. pleasantly relaxed   2

THE DRIVE TO THE OFFICE

Barry yanks open the garage doors, jumps
into his car, and backs hastily out of the
driveway. Hunching forward over the wheel,
he clutches it tightly and stares fixedly
ahead at the road.

A car starts to pull out in front of Barry.
He honks his horn and yells at the driver.
Then he curses as a child runs across the
street, forcing him to slam on the brakes.

Barry Stone acts as if pedestrians and
other drivers were

1. nonexistent.

2. friendly fellow citizens.

3. enemies threatening his security.   3

The lights on the boulevard are timed to
permit traffic to flow steadily at 30 m.p.h.
Barry accelerates to 55 and gets caught by
every light. Each time he stares intensely
at the light, muttering "Come on, come on."
When the light changes, he jams the
accelerator down as if beginning a race.

Do you think that all this haste will get
Barry to the office any faster?   probably not

Barry is stopped again while the police deal
with an accident. He squirms, mutters,
lights a cigarette, races the motor, and
glances at his watch every few seconds.

Does Barry's impatient behavior affect the
passage of time?   no

The accident is finally cleared away, but
Barry is caught in the ensuing traffic jam.
He is half an hour late to work. The boss
asks to speak with him.

Would you say that Barry enjoyed his drive
to work?   no

Has he faced any great problems or any really   Most of our
difficult decision thus far in his day?   readers
                                                   answered no.

Do you accomplish anything by reacting   no
strongly to situations--such as traffic jams--   (Far from
over which you have no control?   providing a
                                                   healthy release
                                                   from tension,
                                                   such reactions
                                                   merely increase
                                                   your sense of
                                                   frustration.)

Would you describe Barry's mood thus far
as tense or relaxed?   tense

Did the energy Barry expended in clutching
the wheel, squirming, muttering, etc., in
any way shorten his trip to the office or
make it more pleasant?   no

THE BOSS

It is now 9:30. Since 9:15 Mr. Bigg has been
waiting for the last tranquilizer to take effect.
He had originally hoped that tranquilizers
would help to reduce his frustrations and prevent
fits of rage, but he still tends to blame employees
for his own emotional disturbances.

Mr. Bigg sometimes wonders whether he should
continue to rely so heavily on tranquilizers. They
do seem to reduce his anxiety over daily problems.
Yet he has a feeling that the number of his
problems is increasing because his thinking is
sometimes a little fuzzy; he doesn't seem to make
decisions as rapidly or as effectively as he did
before he began using tranquilizers. Often he
has to make a positive effort to fight his way back
to some sort of contact with reality.

Mr. Bigg finds that tranquilizers

1. have no effect on him.

2. do him nothing but harm.

3. reduce his tensions so that he can attack
   his problems more vigorously.

4. cause him to worry less, but also
   to function less efficiently.   4

Although he knows that Barry often works
evenings, Mr. Bigg proceeds to give him a
good dressing-down for being late to work.

Barry is sure that his tardiness has done the
business no harm at all, but he apologizes
contritely and promises not to be late again.

After Barry leaves, Mr. Bigg takes a couple of
chalk pills for his peptic ulcer, paces up and down
for ten minutes, and finally sits down at his desk.
At the sight of stacks of papers demanding his
attention, he becomes so nervous that he decides
to take the morning off and play a round of golf.

Mr. Bigg believes that if he remains in his office he will be unable to accomplish an effective morning's work. Would his conduct tend to make you agree with him?

Most readers answered <u>yes</u>.

Mr. Bigg is

1. anticipating his game of golf with pleasure.

2. very sorry to leave his office.

3. substituting golf for a situation in which he is too tense to function adequately.

3

Might some of Mr. Bigg's tension be caused by the knowledge that he attacked Barry Stone unjustly?

yes

Barry feels that he has conducted himself like a miserable weakling. As soon as he gets to his own office, he acts out an imaginary scene in which he tells the boss off. He addresses a series of scathing remarks to the hatrack, and resolves to use them the next time the opportunity presents itself. Recalling the many times that Mr. Bigg has treated him unjustly, he succeeds in working himself up into a self-righteous rage.

Which of the following do you think would have been the most appropriate response for Barry to have made to Mr. Bigg's criticism?

1. To apologize humbly and remain furiously angry, just as he did.

2. To realize that the boss has problems of his own, which are reflected in his attitude this morning, and to pay no further attention to the incident.

3. To shout back at the boss.

2

BARRY STONE'S SECRETARY

Barry rings for his secretary, Marjorie Hall,
and asks to see the letters which he dictated
late the preceding afternoon. Marjorie says
that she hasn't had time to finish them. Barry
answers that a good secretary could have
finished three times as many, and that instead
of her back talk he would like to have whatever
letters she has managed to complete.

The letters which Barry has called for are not
urgent, and he knows that Marjorie has had no
time to finish typing them. When he demands
the letters, Barry is really expressing

1. his long-concealed hatred of Marjorie.

2. genuine rage at her ineptitude.

3. his hatred of office work.

4. his sense of urgency.

5. the hostitlity toward his boss which he
   was afraid to express to Mr. Bigg
   himself.   5

When Barry receives the finished letters, he
complains bitterly of mistakes and omissions
in them. He tells Marjorie that she has been
very inefficient lately, and that if her work
doesn't improve, he will have to dismiss her.

Losing her temper, Marjorie says that she is
tired of working for Barry anyway, and that
she wants to leave at the end of the week. Barry
replies that this course of action will suit him
just fine. As a matter of fact, he says, he will
be very glad to be rid of her.

Barry's decision to discharge his secretary

1. was the result of a carefully worked-out plan.

2. shows that he is always in perfect control of himself.

3. is evidence that he occasionally loses control of himself.

4. will certainly improve the efficiency of his office.   3

When Barry calms down, do you think that he will be happy at the prospect of losing an efficient secretary?   probably not

Assuming that Marjorie likes most aspects of her job, was her response appropriate?   no

It would have been more appropriate for Marjorie to have

1. burst out crying.

2. told Barry that he is less efficient than she.

3. returned to her work, realizing that Barry would soon be sorry for the way he had treated her.

4. stalked out of the office.   3

Barry's tension communicated itself to Marjorie. She became much too tense herself to find an appropriate reaction. Therefore his hostility and aggression elicited similar responses from her.

When you are with tense people, do you tend to become tense yourself?   Most readers answered _yes_.

If you know that three members of a given family are very tense people, would you suspect that the fourth might also be tense?   yes

Might the same be true of members of an office
staff who have worked in close proximity for
many years?   yes

Conversely, when you are with very relaxed
people, do you find that you tend to become   Most readers
more relaxed yourself?   answered yes.

MR. BIGG AND THE POLICEMAN

Since Mr. Bigg is eager to get away from the
office in a hurry, his drive to the golf club is
hardly the pleasant and relaxing experience
it might otherwise have been. In his nervous
haste he exceeds the speed limit, and a policeman motions him to the curb.

Mr. Bigg apologizes, wheedles, pleads ignorance
of the zoned speed limit, and tries every other
sort of excuse, but he receives a ticket anyway.
He drives away almost blind with anger.

All the rest of the way to the golf course, Mr.
Bigg plans elaborate and impossible schemes
of revenge. When policemen have stopped him
in the past, he has sometimes relived the scenes
for weeks.

Mr. Bigg seems to attribute to the scene with
the policeman

    1. too little importance.

    2. exactly the importance it deserves.

    3. too much importance.   3

It would have been more appropriate for Mr.
Bigg to have

    1. insulted the policeman.

    2. realized that the misfortune of being
       stopped was not important enough to
       make him furious with himself and
       the policeman.

    3. given up driving.

    4. thanked the policeman for giving him
       the ticket.   2

MR. BIGG'S GAME OF GOLF

In the locker room at the country club, Mr.
Bigg changes into his golf outfit at top speed.
Half-way to the starter, he finds that he has
no tees. He races back to the pro shop, where
he abuses the assistant pro for selling tiny
packages of tees for a quarter. He notes with
disgust that the shop must be making a "three
thousand percent profit."

Is Mr. Bigg's behavior likely to reduce the
price of tees in the pro shop?   no

The cost of tees probably isn't a serious
concern for anyone belonging to the club; but
assuming that Mr. Bigg does deeply resent
the pro shop's markup, it would be more
reasonable for him simply to

    1. stop using tees.

    2. stop playing golf.

    3. buy his tees in quantity at a discount store

    4. find the pro and complain to him.

    5. go home.   3

Like his tirade at Barry, Mr. Bigg's ranting at
the assistant pro tends to - raise/lower - his   raise
tension level, and to make him a - more/less -   less
congenial person.

Mr. Bigg is equally abusive to the caddy master
when he learns that all the boys are out and
none are expected back for at least twenty minutes.
He resolves to carry his own bag for the first few
holes until a caddy can catch up with him.

People who are very tense seem unable to recognize
or process alternatives. Mr. Bigg has supposedly
taken the morning off to relax. Do you think that in
his present frame of mind he could sit back on the   Probably not. In
clubhouse porch and enjoy the view while he waits   any event he is
for a caddy to come in?   too tense to
                                                            consider the
                                                            possibility.

Although the pro has often cautioned him to
remain relaxed, Mr. Bigg takes a tremendous
tight swing at his first drive. It is as if he were
swinging at his incompetent employees, the
policeman, the assistant pro, the caddy master,
and the absent caddies all at once.

The result is a booming slice which ends up far
out of bounds to the right. Mr. Bigg has started
his round of golf with a lost ball and a penalty.

Do you think that Mr. Bigg's vicious swing at the
ball served to reduce his tension?

probably not

Will the results of his swing cause his feelings
of frustration and tension to increase?

They probably
will.

Will this tend to improve or to impair his game
of golf?

Golf professionals
agree that his
game will suffer.

The caddy appears at the fourth tee. Mr. Bigg
is not having a good round. His dubbed drive
catches the rough some twenty yards in front of
the tee.

The caddy misreads his client and tries to pass
it off with a joke: "Straight as an arrow it rolls,"
he observes philosophically.

Mr. Bigg vents more of his fury on the caddy.
Scowling and hating each other, the two of them
march around the next few holes, while Mr. Bigg
cuts ugly divots in the green turf.

On the seventh hole Mr. Bigg's second shot lands
in a sandtrap to the left of the green. It takes him
five shots to get out. On each of the first four, the
ball catches the overhanging lip of the trap and rolls
serenely back at him. The fifth shot goes completely
over the green.

A golfer who is - calm and relaxed/angry and
frustrated - has a better chance of getting out
of a sandtrap and onto the green.

calm and
relaxed

If Mr. Bigg weren't thinking of the hostile
caddy watching him, he would probably play

1. a better game of golf.

2. the same game.

3. a worse game.   1

The eighth is a water hole. Instead of trying
to play it short, Mr. Bigg puts all his accumulated
fury into an effort to carry it with his drive.
The ball lands in the water.

Mr. Bigg tries again. His second drive also
lands in the water.

Mr. Bigg plays his third drive safe, short of
the water. But he tops his next shot, and it
too goes into the water. He hurls his club after
the ball and stalks back to the clubhouse, with
his smirking caddy trailing behind him.

Does Mr. Bigg seem to have found relaxation
and peace of mind in his round of golf?   no

Are all the activities which our society terms
"recreation" necessarily relaxing?   no

Even when he plays very badly, might Mr. Bigg
adopt a different attitude toward his golf game?   yes

He might view the game as beneficial exercise,
or as a pleasant and relaxing stroll through a
world of green.

Most of Mr. Bigg's waking hours are spent in the
highly competitive business world. His attitude
toward "leisure time" activity reflects the view
of life which he has developed at work. Even
when playing by himself, he thinks of golf as a
competitive game. This is the result of

1. the essential nature of the game of golf.

2. the companions with whom Mr. Bigg
   usually plays.

3. Mr. Bigg's inability to relax and change
   his attitude with a change of scene.

4. the attitude of Mr. Bigg's caddy.   3

TRANSCRIBING DICTATION

Jane McDermott, Mr. Bigg's secretary, is
having certain minor problems of her own.
Mr. Bigg is proud of the large number of
letters which he can record on a single
dictabelt. He speaks at top speed, without
any indication of punctuation, paragraphing,
or the spelling of proper names.

As a result, Jane has to listen to each letter
several times before she finally deciphers its
meaning and makes an initial rough draft. She
tries to make up for lost time by typing as fast
as possible.

Jane's neck is permanently cocked at an angle
suitable for copying rough drafts and looking
up words in a dictionary. Her right foot is
poised over the pedal of her transcribing unit.
Her left is wrapped around a rung of the chair.

Jane wears a constant frown, her jaw muscles
are always tight, and she often unconsciously
grinds her teeth. Her whole body gives the
appearance of uncomfortable tension.

Jane drinks between ten and fifteen cups of
black coffee a day. She takes aspirin frequently
for head and neck aches.

Do you think that the angle at which Jane holds
her neck improves her work in any way?   probably not

Does the strained position of Jane's left foot
improve her typing?   no

Does grinding her teeth help her to grind out
more work?   no

Might she be more comfortable if she knew how
to relax those parts of her body which are not
engaged in actual work?   yes

Might she have less tendency to suffer from neck aches if she stood up and stretched occasionally?

yes

Much of Jane's energy is being dissipated in activities which do not further her work. Which of the following solutions seems best calculated to make her permanently more efficient and more comfortable with herself?

1. Drink more coffee and take more aspirin.

2. Give up the job.

3. At the risk of losing her position, tell Mr. Bigg that he's going to have to learn how to dictate.

4. Adopt a much more relaxed attitude toward her work.

5. Insist on taking Mr. Bigg's dictation in shorthand.

4

If Jane learns to relax, she will become more accurate and more productive. She will learn to work at a steady but comfortable pace and to rest during lunch and coffee breaks. If it is then apparent that her work load is too great to be handled by a single person, Mr. Bigg will probably

1. fire her.

2. hire an assistant for her.

2

WRITER'S CRAMP

Barry Stone is preparing a manual for the use of all salesmen in the company. He has been working on the manual for four months. During this time he has written only a short introduction which he revises continually. The manual is due at the printer's in two weeks.

Barry sits with his feet tucked far back under his chair and his head low over a yellow pad. Although he is expert in the subject matter of the manual, he seems to be making no great progress.

Barry's right hand holds a pencil so tightly that it leaves an indentation in his middle finger. His left hand alternately clutches the yellow pad, scratches his head, drums on the desk, or picks at his face. Almost unconsciously he goes through a pack of cigarettes a day, taking a few puffs on each one, then crushing it out.

Barry is very active while he sits at his desk. Does any of his activity seem to further the preparation of the manual?   no

Barry knows that the manual he is writing has a purely functional purpose. It certainly will not be criticized for literary style. But he feels the eyes of his former English teachers staring coldly over his shoulder at the yellow pad.

Every few minutes Barry leaves his desk to pace up and down, stare out of the window, get a cup of coffee, or demand that his secretary bring him something from the files. He finds it hard to force himself to return to the desk. When he does, words are written and words are crossed out, but the manuscript grows no longer.

Even when preparing material for an uncritical audience, Barry finds writing - easy/difficult.   difficult

Which of the following best describes Barry writing at his desk?

1. tired and sleepy.

2. relaxed and comfortable.

3. tense but productive, with all his energy directed toward a single goal.

4. tense but unproductive, with most of his energy dissipated in random, anxiety-reducing activity.   4

For Barry, the yellow pad on his desk
constitutes

1. a welcome challenge.

2. a source of anxiety.

3. just another routine job.

4. a diversion.   2

Even when he is alone in his office, Barry
seems to be

1. in complete command of himself
   and his environment.

2. half asleep.

3. carelessly happy.

4. locked in battle with an invisible
   opponent.   4

BARRY STONE AT LUNCH

Finally Marjorie announces a visitor. It is
a client with whom Barry has arranged a
luncheon appointment.

With a feeling of relief, Barry pushes the
yellow pad aside and hurries his guest down
to the restaurant on the bottom floor. There
the two of them gulp down cocktails while
arguing the pros and cons of a possible deal.
When the waitress returns, they order another
round of cocktails and the special luncheon,
without looking up. They pay no attention to
their food, but the act of eating seems to
interfere with their conversation. They
swallow each bite rapidly, so that they can
continue talking.

After twenty minutes of debate, Barry and his
guest reach an impasse. Barry agrees to ask
his company's research department for further
details, and they part, leaving their meals half
finished on their plates.

Barry disposed of his cocktails by

   1. sipping them in slow enjoyment.

   2. refusing to drink them.

   3. gulping them down.   3

Barry ate

   1. slowly and with pleasure.

   2. in rapid bites and swallows.   2

He finished

   1. all of his lunch.

   2. part of his lunch.

   3. none of his lunch.   2

Back on his own floor of the building, Barry meets Jane McDermott, who asks what he had for lunch. Barry can't remember. He returns to his office, where he resumes his nervous pacing up and down, thinking of the deal he discussed at lunch, and casting occasional guilty glances at the yellow pad on his desk.

Did Barry seem to enjoy his lunch?   no

Do you think that the lunch satisfied Barry's need for a break in his routine?   probably not

Did Barry even seem to notice his lunch?   no

Barry didn't have to devote his entire lunch hour to the discussion of a business deal. He might have chosen to meet his client in the office before or after lunch, or to take him to a leisurely luncheon in which discussion of business topics was interspersed with pleasant small talk. Would either of these alternatives have permitted Barry to derive some relaxation and enjoyment from his lunch hour?   yes

If Barry and his client had adopted a more
relaxed attitude toward their luncheon,
could they have transacted the same
amount of business?   probably

Is it possible that a more relaxed and
leisurely treatment of the business deal
might have led both men to consider
aspects, alternatives, or solutions which
their states of tension caused them to
overlook?   yes

Might both men have then remained more
relaxed and performed more efficiently
throughout the day?   yes

From what you know of Barry's day thus
far, would you predict that he will write   He probably
effectively this afternoon?   won't.

THE SPECTATOR SPORT

At about one o'clock, a colleague named
Bill Martin steps into Barry's office.
Bill has decided that it is much too hot to
work and that he needs some relaxation.
He invites Barry to join him in an afternoon
at the ball park.

It is warm in the office, and Barry would
ordinarily seize upon any excuse to leave
his work for a baseball game. But he is
still smarting from Mr. Bigg's tongue
lashing, and he is beginning to be really
frightened at the prospect of not finishing
the manual. He therefore admits regretfully
that he has too much work to do.

The fact is that Barry

1. looks forward to working on the
   manual.

2. hates baseball.

3. feels guilty and trapped by the
   unchanging yellow pad on his desk.   3

Do you think that it would really have made
much difference in Barry's output for the
day if he had gone to the ball park instead
of remaining at his desk?   probably not

Barry forces himself to stay in the office
from 1:30 until almost 2:30, but he spends
most of this time pacing and smoking. At
2:30 he suddenly remembers that there is
a conference scheduled. The subject has
little to do with him, and he is not required
to attend, but he stuffs the yellow pad into
his desk drawer and hurries out.

Barry goes to the conference because of

1. his sense of duty to the company.

2. the unbearable tension he feels in
    his office.

3. his eagerness to learn something new.   2

The conference provides him with

1. a temporary escape from a situation
    in which he feels inadequate.

2. help in the preparation of the manual.

3. a permanent escape from the task of
    writing the manual.   1

Meanwhile Bill Martin has lunched at the ball
park on three hot dogs and two cans of beer.
Sitting in the hot sun and perspiring profusely,
he waves his arms and cheers vociferously for
the home club. He also hurls insults at the
officials and at the members of the visiting
team.

Is it really cooler at the ball park than it was
at work?   apparently not

While he is at the ball park, Bill Martin
seems to be interested principally in

1. succeeding in his lifetime
   occupation.

2. identifying vicariously with the
   success of the home team.

3. his physical well-being.   2

It has been twenty years since Bill himself
took any exercise, but he enjoys watching
other men play basketball, football, and
above all baseball. He leaps to his feet
each time his team makes a hit, and wrings
his hands in despair when one of his favorites
strikes out. He places bets with a man seated
beside him and with another behind him in the
stands. By the eighth inning, his team is two
runs behind. There are two outs and three
men on base; a pinch hitter is at bat.

With the count at three and two, Bill's hero
drives two long fouls into the stands before
he finally succeeds in hitting a home run out
of the park. The stands go wild, and Bill is
as wild as anyone.

When the spectators resume their seats,
someone notices that Bill has fallen unconscious.
A doctor is summoned. He says that Bill has
suffered a heart attack, and rushes his patient
to the hospital.

Many of us confuse relaxation with changing
from one activity to another. Was Bill Martin
at least as tense and active at the ball park as
he would have been at his office?   yes

Bill Martin spends several weeks in the hospital, but he recovers and is permitted to return to work. His doctor tells him to take mild exercise, but to avoid excitement and strain. In the doctor's opinion, it would have been better if Bill had channeled his athletic interests in the direction of

1. more interesting spectator sports.

2. regular moderate exercise, such as daily walks.

3. active participation in strenuous, competitive sports, such as football and basketball.

4. watching baseball on television.   2

MR. BIGG'S LECTURE

Mr. Bigg is scheduled to give a lecture at a late luncheon of the Junior Chamber of Commerce. During the luncheon, he is much too preoccupied in rehearsing his speech to notice what he eats.

When the time comes for him to talk, Mr. Bigg paces back and forth, with his notes clutched tightly in his shaking right hand. His left hand alternately mops his perspiring brow and jingles coins in his pocket. His voice is harsh and metallic.

When Mr. Bigg speaks, his body is

1. relaxed and still.

2. in constant motion.   2

His voice is

1. grating and strident.

2. low and calm.

3. soft and pleasant.   1

It is Mr. Bigg's intention to project a pleasant
image of himself and his company. He knows
that in order to do this he must give due credit
to his suppliers, competitors, and customers.
Nevertheless, he finds himself launching into a
tirade against the dishonesty and inefficiency of
the other companies in his field. His remarks
irritate and wound many of those present and
finally antagonize the entire audience.

In the discussion period which follows his talk,
Mr. Bigg's views are attacked, and he defends
his position bitterly.

Did Mr. Bigg's speech accomplish his purpose?   no

Might it have been better for Mr. Bigg's
company and for his temper if he hadn't
spoken at all?   yes

Even if Mr. Bigg succeeds in winning most of
the ensuing arguments, do you think that he
will gain the sympathy of his audience and secure
new friends for his company?   no

Since Mr. Bigg wanted to find potential
customers among the members of his audience,
his best policy would have been to

1. demonstrate what a brilliant lecturer he
    is, and what a cutting wit he has.

2. understate his case so that the members
    of the audience would be tempted to state
    it in stronger terms, and he would then be
    able to agree with what they said.

3. demonstrate aggressively how much better
    his company is than all others in the field.

4. refrain from mentioning his company, but
    attack all others in the field.   2

During the question and answer period,
Mr. Bigg should have

1. dominated the scene completely.

2. refused to answer any questions
    at all.

3. shown an understanding of the
    various aspects of his subject,
    while giving the others present
    a chance to express their views.   3

In order to do this, Mr. Bigg needed to
have

1. complete control over the other
    people.

2. enough control over himself to
    maintain a relaxed awareness
    of the situation.

3. a superb vocabulary and a sparkling
    personality.   2

Nervous speakers are often unable to maintain
an objective viewpoint. Like Mr. Bigg, when
he devoted all his energy to abusing his
competitors, they lose sight of their major
goal and become emotionally involved in the
presentation of a single aspect of an argument.
As a result, they devote their time to

1. trying to justify themselves and
    prove how right they are.

2. trying to achieve their major objective.

3. trying to give others a chance to express
    themselves.   1

MRS. STONE'S DAY

Jean Stone usually rises earlier than her
husband to wake the children, get them
dressed, prepare their breakfast, start
them off to school, serve her husband's
breakfast, and help him on his way.

Today, shortly after Barry leaves for work,
the TV repairman arrives. Jean complains
that the set is broken again, after having had
expensive repair work only three weeks ago.
The repairman tells her this sort of thing is
bound to happen if she insists on buying cheap
models. He assures her that the only solution
is to trade in her set for a more expensive one
at his store.

Jean finds the man's remarks exasperating and
his attitude insolent, but she can't think of a
suitable reply. She retreats in embarrassment
to the kitchen where she divides the rest of the
morning between washing clothes and thinking of
ways to "tell the repairman off."

Jean Stone is obviously

1. paying too little attention to the
   repairman's words.

2. paying too much attention to his
   words and upsetting herself
   needlessly.

3. paying his words exactly the attention
   they deserve and preparing an adequate
   reply for the next time she finds herself
   in a similar situation.   2

At lunch the children seem unusually boisterous.
After Jean has sent them back to school, she
takes an aspirin, gets into her small foreign car,
and drives off to shop.

Jean needs a roast for dinner and some other
cuts of meat for the weekend. She finds
exactly what she wants, but for some reason
prices appear unusually high. She complains
at length to the butcher.

Although Jean has always been highly satisfied
with her purchases in this particular store, she
becomes so angry that she finally attacks not
only the cost of the meat but also its quality.
When the butcher protests, Jean stamps out of
the shop without buying anything.

The fact is that Jean Stone

1. has suddenly realized that the meat in
   her favorite store is exorbitantly priced.

2. is venting some of the hostility carried
   over from her frustrating experience in
   dealing with the TV repairman.

3. is expressing her strongly developed
   sense of justice.   **2**

If Jean really thought that her butcher was
selling meat at inordinately high prices, it
would seem most appropriate for her to

1. tell him about it daily.

2. keep silent about it, no matter
   how much it infuriates her.

3. tell all her friends and neighbors
   about it, and solicit their
   cooperation in boycotting the shop.

4. try another butcher.

5. give up eating meat.   **4**

As she leaves the butcher shop, Jean meets
an old friend whose husband is president of
the Young Democrats in town. Jean herself
is a staunch Republican. The two women
begin a discussion of local politics, from
which they branch into state and national
issues. Their voices become louder and louder.

After an hour the women part, each muttering
to herself that the other is a stubborn fool.

Arguments with convinced opponents about
abstract political issues are likely to lead to

1. sudden conversions.

2. losing time and friends.

3. saving the world.

4. reforming the local political scene.

5. more efficient shopping.

2

Back at the car, Jean takes two more aspirins.
She decides not to attempt any more shopping.
It is only 3 in the afternoon, but Jean feels that
she has had a very trying day. She wonders
why so many disagreeable things always happen
to her. Her only concern now is getting home
where she can lie down.

But Jean is unable to start her car. She has to
call a foreign car garage. The mechanic is
busy; he tells her that he doesn't like to leave
his shop in the middle of the day.

Jean insists that the mechanic come at once.
He arrives about half an hour later, only to
receive a tongue lashing for having taken so
long.

Jean asks how soon the car can be repaired.
The mechanic answers that it takes time to get
parts for foreign cars. Jean says that finding
the parts is his problem, and that she wants
her car by the following day.

The mechanic knows that Jean's car needs
only a new battery, which he has in stock, but
he is annoyed by her attitude. He tells her
the car won't be ready until Monday.

When Jean finds that there is no other foreign
car garage in the vicinity, she leaves the car
with the mechanic and takes a cab home. As
soon as she gets there, she goes to bed with
an icepack over her eyes.

Are at least some of Jean's problems caused
as much by herself as by external agents?   yes

Is an expression of hostility toward another
person likely to bring a hostile reply?   yes

People who are very tense and preoccupied
with their own problems are

1. very good at seeing things from
    another person's point of view.

2. usually unable to consider the other
    person.

3. comfortable people to be around.   2

THE COCKTAIL HOUR

Barry's conference is over at 3:30. He
manages to waste 15 more minutes
chatting in the corridor. He then returns
to his office and stares at the yellow pad
until 5 o'clock.

Barry makes it a practice to stop at a
nearby bar before going home. He and his
colleagues slouch over the bar, wrap their
legs around the barstools, and grip their
glasses tightly in both hands. In strident
voices they recite the various injustices
experienced during the day. Barry attacks
Mr. Bigg; two others immediately defend
him. The result is a violent argument.

The men's strained positions and loud voices
give evidence of - tension/relaxation.   tension

Barry and his friends seem to be

1. enjoying their drinks.

2. enjoying a friendly discussion.

3. concerned with topics of international
    importance.

4. tying themselves in knots around the
    bar rail.

5. practicing complete relaxation.   4

The drinks make them

1. happier.
2. openly hostile.
3. more relaxed.
4. tired.   2

They seem to recount only

1. grievances.
2. jokes.
3. plans.
4. new ideas.   1

The argument increases in volume. Finally
a huge stranger on Barry's right tells them
all to shut up. Barry replies that some people
just can't seem to mind their own business.
The stranger grabs Barry and tells him to get
out and to take his buddies with him.

Barry turns white and his friends shrink down
on their barstools. To their great relief the
bartender appears, admonishes them, and
restores peace.

After muttering self-consciously for a few
minutes, Barry and his friends slink away.
In front of the bar they devote another
fifteen minutes to justifying their retreat.
Several admit ruefully that they have promised
their wives not to get into any more fights.
All agree that people like the huge stranger
should not be allowed to roam loose in society.
They decide that they could easily have handled
him if the bartender had not interfered. They
then break up to find their cars.

Barry and his friends went to the bar to
"relax." Did their approach to a sociable
cocktail hour help them to escape the
tensions of the working day?   no

Did they seem to enjoy their experience
in the bar?   no

An objective observer might wonder why
Barry's group continues to enact this daily
barroom scene. Tense people are unable
to view their behavior patterns objectively.
We might therefore predict that even after
today's incident Barry and his friends
probably will

   1. continue to meet after work to indulge
      in cocktails and petty grievances.

   2. never take another drink.

   3. tend to avoid drinking in bars.   1

HOME SWEET HOME

Barry arrives home at 6:30. Jean complains
that he has again forgotten to pick up some
badly needed plugs and extension cords from
the hardware store. He tells her that she
might do better to concentrate on her own
tasks.

Think of people whom you would classify as
tense. Are they often so preoccupied with
their own problems that they forget their
telephone numbers, license plate numbers,
the names of new acquaintances, or small   Most readers
tasks which they have promised to perform?   answered yes.

To avoid the shrieking children, Barry hides
in his bedroom with a newspaper. Nothing
daunted, one of the boys comes howling in
after him. Barry tells him to shut up and go
away. The boy screams louder. Barry spanks
him.

Jean rushes to the scene. Barry realizes that
he has been striking the boy very hard, and his
guilt makes him react violently toward his wife.
He pushes them both out of the room and locks
the door.

Barry often complains that his work makes him
nervous. Tense people tend to overreact to
annoyances. Might it be Barry's high level of
tension which makes him unable to stand the
children's noise?   yes

Noisy children, in turn, react badly to neglect,
and tend to make even louder noises in hopes of
attracting attention. If Barry joined his
children when he returned from work, they
would probably

    1. tear him to pieces.

    2. be less tense, noisy, and demanding.

    3. shriek even louder.

    4. think their father crazy.   2

Will a higher level of tension in the children
tend to lead to more tension in Barry, and
vice versa?   yes

THE MEAL

Dinner is at 7:30. Jean loads the children's
plates with foods which she considers nourishing.
While keeping up a constant stream of complaints,
she tries to force each child to eat everything on
his plate. The children protest, scream, cry,
and spill things.

Unable to stand the din and finding no way to put
an end to it, Barry swallows his food in five
minutes and leaves to put on his bowling shirt.
The league in which his team competes isn't
scheduled to bowl until 9 o'clock, but he feels
that he will go mad if he doesn't get out of the
house.

How many of the following changes in attitude
might have helped to make dinner at the Stones
more of a success?

   1. Mrs. Stone's realization that nagging at
      your children may make them hate you
      and raise their tension level, but that it
      doesn't improve their behavior.

   2. Her realization that children should not
      be forced to eat large amounts of food
      which they dislike.

   3. Barry's realization that even the most
      lovable children occasionally cry and
      spill things.

   4. The whole family's realization that
      mealtime is meant for relaxation
      and the slow enjoyment of food.   all four of these

It seems probable that the young Stones will
grow up to view meals as

   1. festive occasions.

   2. anxiety-producing situations

   3. periods of comfortable relaxation

   4. opportunities to savor food.   2

Do Jean and Barry Stone seem to be
communicating their tensions to the
children?   yes

THE BOWLERS

Barry's bowling team is made up of members
of his company's office staff. While the players
await their turns, they talk about their work, the
only subject which they have in common. They
discuss various aspects of company policy, swap
stories about their secretaries and bosses, complain
of difficulties with their clients, etc.

When Barry goes to the bowling alley, he

1. forgets everything but the game.

2. changes his working environment completely.

3. takes part of his working environment with him.

3

Someone shouts that it's Barry's turn. He apologizes for not paying attention, hurries to the rack, nervously selects his ball, and takes his position to bowl.

Barry is a spot bowler. Trying not to think of the onlookers, he rivets his gaze on the mark at which he will aim his ball. He crouches, jiggles the ball for a moment, makes a false start, resumes his crouch, jiggles the ball again, finally makes a four-step approach and releases the ball with a twist of his wrist that imparts a powerful spin to it.

As Barry watches the ball go down the alley, he sees that it is hooking to the left of the headpin. He twists his body grotesquely to the right, as if trying to pull the ball over. But it crosses far to the left, and he is left with a nasty split.

While waiting for his ball to return, Barry indulges in some strong language and resolves to take more time in his next approach. As a result he does pick up the split, but he slides over the foul line in doing so, and the spare doesn't count. Cursing his luck, he returns to receive various suggestions from his well-meaning teammates.

Does Barry show signs of tension as he prepares to bowl?

yes

Does his awareness of the onlookers affect his concentration?

yes

Barry feels that his poor bowling is a function of

1. his tension.
2. his ineptitude.
3. bad luck.   3

For Barry, bowling seems to be

1. a pleasant form of exercise.
2. an unimportant game.
3. serious, competitive work.
4. an opportunity to relax completely.   3

Barry and his teammates are still arguing
loudly about possible changes in his style
when the next member of the opposing team
steps up to bowl. Unable to concentrate
because of the noise, the bowler comes back
from the alley to complain.

Barry says it's strange that his opponents aren't
bothered by their own noise. A member of the
other team offers to make Barry shut up.

Barry starts toward the other bowler, and both
men have to be restrained. They have become
so tense that neither is able to bowl well for the
rest of the evening.

The tension in all the bowlers

1. is released each time they bowl.
2. shows itself in aggression and hostility.
3. remains hidden inside them.   2

Barry's team loses the third game by only two
pins. They spend half an hour trying to find
mistakes in the scoring and arguing with their
opponents. Changing his shoes in the locker
room, Barry swears that he will never bowl
again.

From what you know of Barry's behavior,
would you predict that he will bowl again
next week?

He probably
will.

Does bowling seem to bring him rest and
freedom from tension?

no

It seems to offer him only

1. some change in activity.

2. complete relaxation.

3. a chance to laugh and enjoy himself.　1

Barry might find bowling much more enjoyable
if he

1. improved his style.

2. joined another team.

3. took a more relaxed attitude toward the
game.

4. bowled more often.　3

Barry's goal in bowling should be

1. winning.

2. enjoying himself.

3. developing a professional style.　2

THE DATE

Marjorie Hall, Barry's secretary, has been
reproaching herself for having lost her job.
Fortunately she now has something else to
think about--a blind date for the movies with
a friend of her roommate named Ted Buchanan.

The thought of exposing herself to a new person's
evaluation both thrills and frightens Marjorie.
She spends considerable time getting ready, and
twice changes her mind about the dress she will
wear.

When her roommate introduces Ted, Marjorie
is so nervous at the thought of his judging her
that she finds it hard to look at him or talk to
him. The things she does find to say are not so
much thoughtful answers to his remarks as
attempts to impress him with her wit.

Marjorie is far too worried about what Ted
will think of her to notice that he is at least
equally nervous. Each of them tries to say
clever things, but neither can listen to the
other well enough to ask relevant questions.
As a result there is no real communication
between them, and they learn very little about
one another.

For Marjorie, a blind date is

1. a relaxing experience.

2. a sickening experience.

3. a tension-producing experience.

4. just a bore.   3

Her greatest concern is with

1. the young man's looks.

2. his intelligence.

3. his opinion of her.

4. her opinion of him.   3

On the way to the movie, Ted suggests that
they stop somewhere for a cocktail. Marjorie
is not particularly fond of drinking, but this
suddenly seems to be a wonderful idea. She
finishes her first drink before the waiter can
leave the table. She feels embarrassed until
she notices that Ted's glass is also empty.
He quickly orders another round of drinks which
disappear in the same fashion. Then the
conversation flows more easily.

Alcohol has

1. no effect on a person's feeling of tension.

2. a tendency to reduce tension.

3. a tendency to increase tension.   2

Tense people tend to eat and drink very
- rapidly/slowly.   rapidly

Marjorie smokes a cigarette, fidgets with
her empty glass, and chatters about the
loss of her job and other details of her life,
which she suddenly feels must be extremely
interesting.

Ted isn't listening. He is too busy smoking,
fiddling with his glass, and trying to think of
interesting details of his own life to interject
when given an opportunity.

Inability to listen to another person is often
a manifestation of - tension/relaxation.   tension

Are little, meaningless movements, such as
fingering objects on a table, also signs of
tension?   yes

Marjorie and Ted leave the bar. Each
sustains a one-sided conversation as they
walk to the movie.

The show is billed as a "mystery thriller."
Marjorie finds it really terrifying, but it
is a relief from the strain of her self-
conscious conversation with Ted.

After the movie, Marjorie insists that she
must go straight home and get some sleep.
She does go to bed right after Ted leaves
her at the door. But she is still disturbed
by the movie and worried about what Ted
might have thought of her. She tosses until
three in the morning before finally dropping
into a light, restless sleep.

For Marjorie, the mystery thriller provided

1. release from a social situation in
   which she was too tense to be
   comfortable.

2. relaxation among pleasant company.

3. uncomplicated spectator amusement.   1

If she had been less tense throughout the evening,
might Marjorie have enjoyed her date more?   yes

Might she also have been less worried about
the impression she was making?   yes

Would she then have created a more favorable   Most readers
impression?   answered yes.

If you are involved in tension-producing
situations during the evening, will you be
prepared to relax and sleep later?   no

Do you think that Ted fell asleep soon after
he arrived home?   probably not

Why not?   Throughout the
                                                     evening he
                                                     seemed as tense
                                                     as Marjorie.

THE BRIDGE PLAYERS

The Biggs have been invited to the Uptons for
an after-dinner game of bridge. The two
couples often play for relatively high stakes.
Since they are reasonably well matched, very
little money changes hands. Nevertheless the
attitude of the players is highly competitive.

Biting their lips and mopping their foreheads,
the two men stare intently at their cards.
Occasionally one of the wives makes an attempt
at conversation in a high-pitched, nervous voice.
Inevitably she is silenced by her husband.

Do the Biggs seem to find bridge exciting?   yes

Do they play a relaxed game of bridge?   no

Playing bridge offers the Biggs and the
Uptons

1. a chance to laugh and enjoy
   themselves.

2. a complete release from the tensions
   of the day.

3. an escape from the problems of daily
   reality into other problems.   3

At midnight the Biggs realize that it is time
to go home, but they can't seem to stop; the
Uptons join them in insisting on "just one
more rubber."

Pretending surprise that it has grown so late,
the Biggs take their leave at 4 a.m. They rush
home, arguing about how the hands should have
been played, berating each other for mistakes,
and feeling guilty for staying up so long that
neither of them will be "worth anything" in the
morning.

Even when tired children have become so
quarrelsome and irritable that it is hard
to see how they can be enjoying themselves,
they often insist on staying up to continue
playing a game.

In the business world Mr. Bigg and Mr.
Upton are considered to be mature
executives. As bridge players, they
resemble _____ who clench their   children
toys tightly and refuse to give them up,
even though they know it is past their
bedtime.

Does the Bigg-Upton type of bridge game seem
to be a good preparation for sleep?   no

Their bridge game has the two disadvantages
of causing the participants to avoid sleep
deliberately, and of raising their tension
levels so high that they find it hard to sleep
even long after they have stopped playing.
We may suspect that the following morning
will find Mr. Bigg

1. wide awake and cheerful.

2. rested.

3. relaxed and comfortable.

4. feeling guilty, headachy, and irritable.   4

Would you guess that Mr. Bigg's enormous
expenditure of energy on bridge helps or   It probably
hinders him in his daily work?   hinders him.

Might Mr. Bigg live a longer and happier life
if he gave up playing bridge, or if he changed
his competitive attitude toward the game?   yes

THE STIMULATING BOOK

Meanwhile Mr. Bigg's secretary, Jane
McDermott, has prudently declined an
invitation to a party and gone to bed right
after dinner, intending to read herself to
sleep. Her book, a bestseller, proves
so interesting that she is still reading
at 2 a.m., although her eyes feel as if
they were burning in their sockets.

Jane has propped herself up with pillows,
but instead of leaning back easily against
them she unconsciously supports herself
by keeping parts of her body in a state of
tension. As the story grips her, her
tension level increases and her breathing
becomes rapid and shallow; she stares
unblinkingly at the page, while her straining
eyes water constantly.

Deciding that she must get some sleep, Jane
resolutely closes the book. But her eyes
seem to be trying to stare through the closed
lids at scenes from the novel. Jane hears
4:30 strike before she finally goes to sleep.

Is reading in bed always a good way to put
yourself to sleep?   no

While reading in bed. Jane shows a number
of symptoms of - relaxation/tension.   tension

Might it be both more enjoyable and better
for her general health if she were sufficiently
relaxed to allow herself to blink her eyes often,
breathe regularly, and lie back comfortably
against the pillows?   yes

Since Jane really wanted to go to sleep, she
should have chosen to read

1. some work from the office which she
   had brought home.

2. the most interesting story of romance
   or adventure that she could find.

3. a non-fiction work with no real relation
   to her daily problems.

4. a detective story or science-fiction thriller.   3

THE QUARREL

Barry arrives home at 11:30. Jean is
drinking a highball and watching television.
She complains that he might spend a little
more time at home with her and the children.

Barry says that he comes home looking for a
quiet place to rest, not for a madhouse full
of screaming children. Jean replies that she
has to put up with a lot more than he does.
She then launches into a long list of grievances
which include lack of money, lack of attention,
lack of variety, lack of affection, and a great
number of other lacks.

When she attacks her husband for his
shortcomings, Jean Stone is really
expressing unhappiness resulting from
tension within

1. her husband.

2. the television set.

3. their home.

4. herself.   4

Thus she blames Barry for her own problems.
If she really wants to be happy, it would be
better for her to

1. try to change Barry.

2. get a divorce.

3. modify her own attitudes.

4. take a vacation.   3

If Jean could control her own emotional
reactions, it would be silly for her to
blame someone else for a state of mind
which she herself could change. Since she
hasn't learned to control her emotions, she
will probably find the best course is to

1. study the techniques of relaxation
    which lead to self-control.

2. try to control her entire environment
    so that only "good things" happen to her.

3. teach Barry to control his reactions.

4. punish the children whenever they
    are noisy.   1

Barry has been compiling his own list of
injustices. He paces heavily back and forth,
waves his arms, bangs his fist on a table,
and recounts the wrongs his wife has done
him. Jean interrupts him to shriek answers
to his accusations. His voice rises in pitch
and volume. The noise awakens the children,
who clamor for attention.

At this, Jean stalks out to mix another drink,
slamming the door behind her. Barry follows,
and they argue for another half hour in the
kitchen. When they have talked themselves
out, they go back into the living room, take up
their places before the television set, and
watch a late movie.

During the argument Barry devoted his full
attention to

1. listening to Jean's complaints.

2. the silliness of the whole quarrel.

3. establishing a stronger case against
    Jean.   3

Was Jean thinking only of accusations which
she could hurl at Barry?   yes

Assuming that there is some justification on
both sides, will this approach to the situation
ever lead to a more compatible relationship?   probably not

WATCHING TELEVISION

Before learning how to relax, you are likely
to find yourself in one of the following
situations when watching television:

(1) On the rare occasions when a good
program is presented, you become
interested, stimulated, and highly
involved.

(2) You keep switching from one bad
program to another, but since you
know that there is a remote possibility
of striking a good program, you do
not turn the set off; like a slot machine
player, you keep turning the selector
knob and hoping for the payoff.

(3) You are forced to admit that the entire
selection for the evening is bad, and
you become very annoyed at a medium
which spends so much money only to
bore you.

In sullen and hostile silence, the Stones sit
and stare at the TV set. Finally Barry can
stand it no longer. Declaring that the show
is idiotic, he tries another channel.

Five minutes later, Jean switches channels.
They try another and still another program.
Both lament the low quality of television
entertainment, but they seem unable to turn
the set off and go to bed.

Like the Biggs with their game of bridge, or
Jane McDermott with her best-seller, the
Stones have devoted their late evening hours to

1. actively fighting sleep.

2. sleeping.

3. relaxing in hopes of becoming sleepy.   1

Finally Barry says that he has to finish some
work and leaves for his desk in the bedroom.
Do you think that Barry will write more easily
at home than he did at the office?   probably not

After half an hour of knitting his brows, writing
occasional phrases, and then crossing them out,
Barry pushes the yellow pad aside, undresses
quickly, and throws himself into bed.

Does it seem likely that he will fall asleep
immediately?   no

Barry cannot escape the tensions from the
quarrel and the frustrating experience of
trying to write. Visions of the unfinished
manual, the annoying events of the day, the
problems that await him in the morning, and
the programs he watched on television race
through his head. He groans, sighs, and
tosses restlessly from one side of the bed to
the other.

Will Barry have any useful thoughts during
this late period of wakefulness?   probably not

At 2 a.m. Jean abandons the television set.
She has still another drink in the hope that
the nightcap will make it easier for her to
sleep.

When Jean turns on the light by the bed,
Barry complains that he is finding it easy
enough to stay awake without her help.
Later Jean asks him to stop tossing and
moaning so that she, at least, will have a
chance to sleep. Both remain wide awake.

The Stones are both

1. persecuted people.

2. voicing honest complaints.

3. petulantly sustaining the quarrel
    because neither is sufficiently
    relaxed to sleep, and because each
    derives some small satisfaction
    from attacking the other.   3

At 3:30 a.m. the Stones are still awake. Jean
gets sleeping tablets and a glass of water.
They take the pills, toss a while longer, and
finally fall into a drugged sleep.

If a person suffers from insomnia, is it a
good practice for him to do office work just
before going to bed?   no

Is watching television an effective way for
most people to put themselves to sleep?   no

After you have gone to bed, will rehashing
your personal and business problems help
you to sleep?   no

When you deliberately enter into and prolong
a pointless quarrel with your spouse, you are
expressing primarily

1. your own feelings of frustration.

2. your dissatisfaction with the other
   person.

3. your hatred of marriage.

4. your love of a good fight.   1

SOME CHARACTER TRAITS

Select the words which seem to describe the
characters you have just read about:

tense	tense
nervous	nervous
serene	
inconsiderate	inconsiderate
happy	
angry	angry
cheerful	
hostile	hostile
unhappy	unhappy
objective	
irritable	irritable
relaxed	
open-minded	
anxious	anxious

confident

worried   worried

tired   tired

smiling

hopeful

selfish   selfish

despondent   despondent

satisfied

rested

insecure   insecure

frustrated   frustrated

assured

irrational   irrational

comfortable

friendly

likeable

quarrelsome   quarrelsome

Have you recognized in your own acquaintances some of the character traits of Mr. Bigg, the Stones, Jane McDermott, Marjorie Hall, and Bill Martin?

All our readers answered <u>yes</u>.

Have you even recognized some of the same tendencies in yourself?

If not, you're an exceptional person.

Do you believe that anyone who had a conscious choice in the matter would wish to resemble Barry Stone or Mr. Bigg?

All our readers answered <u>no</u>.

Mr. Bigg feels that he has no choice. He believes that his belligerence and spite are caused by difficulties

1. within himself.

2. in the outside world.   2

Do some of Mr. Bigg's frustrations result
from problems which originate in him rather
than in his environment?   yes

Do problems within Mr. Bigg then cause real
conflicts with his environment?   yes

SELF-IMPORTANCE AS A GOAL

Very early in life, Mr. Bigg decided that he
wanted to become an important man. He has
subordinated everything to the achievement of
that goal.

In order to attain his objective, Mr. Bigg
needs to

1. impress other people.

2. become an intellectual leader.

3. follow a religious career.

4. study philosophy.   1

For the man who wishes only to be important,
a job is

1. a pleasant end in itself.

2. a pathway to knowledge.

3. an obstacle to be surmounted on the
   way up.   3

Mr. Bigg decided that a business career would
be his most direct route to success.   To his
goal of becoming important, he sacrificed his
own happiness as well as that of his family and
his associates at work.   He even sacrificed his
opinion of himself.

Mr. Bigg was sure that greatness existed in the
outside world; anything he did seemed justified if
it made others think him important.   He began by
feeling that his opinion of himself didn't matter,
and finally reached a point where he had no opinion
of himself at all.

Mr. Bigg's goal was to achieve greatness
in the eyes of others. Therefore he had
to accept without question the standards
of his society and to forego setting up any
code of his own. Left without a way of
judging greatness for himself, he could
believe he was important only when others
told him so.

Mr. Bigg's object in life is to become

1. wise.

2. important.

3. happy.   2

For Mr. Bigg, greatness lies

1. within himself.

2. in the opinions of others.   2

Mr. Bigg is engaged in a constant struggle
to impress others with his importance. As
a consequence he can

1. sit back and be satisfied that he
   has reached his goal.

2. never relax and enjoy himself.

3. always be sure he is making a
   good impression.   2

HAPPINESS AS A GOAL

Next door to the Biggs live the Daltons.
Although John Dalton and Everett Bigg were
once classmates in college, they don't see
much of each other any more. This seems
to be a consequence of the dissimilarity of
their goals.

At about the time that Everett Bigg chose to
become important, John Dalton also decided
to devote his entire life to the achievement of
one objective. But John's goal was not self-
importance. Early in life he realized that the
people around him had many different ideas of
greatness, and that these ideas changed from
day to day. He felt that he could never enjoy
himself if he were continually trying to live
in accordance with other people's standards.
And above all John Dalton wanted to enjoy
himself. So he chose happiness as his
personal goal.

Did John Dalton feel that everyone had the
same idea of greatness?   no

Did he feel that it was possible to appear
important to everyone at all times?   no

John took as his goal - greatness/happiness.   happiness

John soon discovered that people had as
many different views of happiness as they
did of greatness. But the majority did seem
to agree that there were a number of things
in the outside world which were inherently
desirable. They believed that happiness
resulted from collecting as many of these
things as possible. Unhappiness consisted
in being deprived of desirable things. If
this view of life were coi rect, all wealthy
people would tend to be - happy/unhappy.   happy

By the same token, all poor people would
necessarily be _____.   unhappy

But as John looked about him in the world,
he found that this was not always the case.
Enjoyment did not seem to depend on how
much or how little people owned. It seemed
less related to the type of experiences a
person had than to the way in which he
interpreted his experiences.

John saw one man delight in a situation which another found extremely painful. He saw one woman happy in a house which another would disdain to live in; he saw one of his friends overjoyed at being able to purchase an old car, and another disgusted with his new car because it wasn't a more expensive model.

John therefore decided that the happiness or unhappiness of an individual is determined not by things or situations, but by the individual himself.

Did John find that happiness consists in accumulating the right sort of external objects?   no

Did he decide that the situation in which a man finds himself makes him happy or unhappy?   no

John concluded that a man's happiness depends on

1. getting the things he wants.

2. the situations in which he is involved.

3. the way in which he perceives and interprets his experiences.   3

For John, happiness is found in

1. oneself.

2. external situations.

3. other people.

4. the accumulation of wealth.   1

John's solution to the problem of human happiness is

1. external and social

2. internal and personal.   2

Let's follow John Dalton through a typical day.

THE EARLY MORNING

John wakes at 7 a. m. after eight hours
of restful sleep. He never uses an alarm
clock, but he makes a habit of going to bed
at 11 and getting up at 7.

John could continue to function if he slept
only seven hours a night; but he has found
that when he sleeps an average of eight
hours he enjoys his life more and is more
creative and efficient. He doesn't make a
practice of recommending any particular
amount of sleep to other people, but he
does suggest that they sleep until they feel
fully rested.

With which of the following statements do
you think John would agree?

1. Everyone should sleep at least eight
    hours a day.

2. Everyone should sleep at least seven
    hours a day.

3. A person should get as much sleep as
    is necessary for him to function well
    and to enjoy his waking hours.

4. A person should try to get along on an
    absolute minimum of sleep.   3

As a teenager, John suffered from insomnia,
but at the age of twenty he learned a series
of techniques of relaxation for putting himself
to sleep. Since that time, his sleep has always
been deep and restful. The few dreams that he
can remember are pleasant ones.

John Dalton tends to sleep - more/less - than   more
Barry Stone.

Does John need to drug himself with pills in
order to sleep?   no

John knows

1. that he needs more sleep than most people.
2. that he can sleep only when physically exhausted.
3. how to relax and put himself to sleep.
4. that no one can learn how to go to sleep.   3

John's sleep is

1. fitful and uneasy.
2. deep and restful.
3. disturbed by nightmares.
4. absolutely dreamless.   2

THE UNHURRIED LIFE

We have already seen that John Dalton - uses/doesn't require - an alarm clock to wake himself up.   doesn't require

When John does wake up, he remains in bed for a few minutes, enjoying the relaxed state of his entire body and looking forward to a pleasant day.

After John gets up, he takes a leisurely shower, dresses without haste, and then eats a slow, relaxed breakfast while chatting with his wife Mary. Because he is well rested, he doesn't need to drink coffee at breakfast to wake up. Nor does he find that he requires it as a stimulant at any time during the day.

In his job as a publicity writer, John has
always insisted on the right to come and
go as he wishes. He might make more
money if he were willing to try to please
a dozen bosses by working frantically
from nine to five, but he feels that he
might also lead a shorter and less enjoyable
life. He has therefore always refused to
subordinate his personal goals to those of
any organization.

After breakfast, John goes for a brief stroll
before getting into his car.

Does John appear nervous and tense as he
starts his day?   no

Does he seem tired?   no

As he goes through his early morning routine,
John

1. races rapidly from one sub-goal to
    another, jumping out of bed, dressing
    hurriedly, gulping down his breakfast,
    and rushing to the office.

2. is too exhausted to have any clear idea
    of what is going on.

3. subordinates everything to his principal
    objective of remaining relaxed and happy
    throughout the day.   3

What we have learned about John thus far
indicates that he

1. always follows the dictates of others.

2. is self-directed.

3. flits rapidly from one project to
    another.   2

ANOTHER WAY TO DRIVE TO WORK

Mary Dalton has asked John to drop her off at a shopping center on his way to work. While he waits for her to come out of the house, he sits comfortably at the wheel of his car and enjoys a conversation with some passing neighbors.

Does John seem capable of waiting without growing restless and ill-tempered?   yes

While waiting, John gives the impression that

1. he is bored.

2. he is uncomfortable.

3. he is enjoying himself so much that he is in no hurry to do anything else.   3

Do you know people who are so afraid of wasting time and always in such a hurry to do something else that they never enjoy the   **Most readers** moment in which they are living?   **answered _yes_.**

If we say that someone is "wasting time," are we assuming that he is in a hurry to attain some external goal?   yes

If your sole goal is happiness, and you are happy, can you be wasting time?   no

When Mary comes out of the house, John compliments her on her appearance and invites her to join in the conversation.

After taking leave of his neighbors, John
starts the car and pulls out from the curb.
He sits back comfortably with both hands
in a relaxed position on the wheel, his left
leg outstretched, and his left foot resting
on the floor. The Daltons talk of how
pleased they are with their new car.

John smiles at other drivers' mistakes and
at his own. When stopped by a red light, he
yawns and stretches comfortably. He pulls
away from traffic lights slowly and smoothly.

The period of heavy early morning traffic is
already over, but a mild snarl ahead forces
the Daltons to come to a brief halt. John
takes advantage of the delay to discuss some
purchases with his wife.

John seems to view driving in traffic as

1. a challenge which demands tight
   control and full attention.

2. a means of getting to his destination
   as fast as possible.

3. a frightening business.

4. an enjoyable form of activity.

5. a dreadful bore.   4

John's position at the wheel of the car
might be described as

1. cramped.

2. relaxed.

3. tense.   2

As the traffic begins to move again, a policeman
waves John through an intersection. On the other
side, John finds himself blocked by a solid line
of traffic. Another policeman upbraids him for
having crossed the intersection.

Mary is very indignant; she wants to point
out to the policeman that it was he or his
colleague who made the mistake.

John simply smiles and finds a way around
the traffic jam. As they drive on, he explains
to Mary that he doesn't see himself as guilty
or inferior; as a consequence he feels no need
to justify himself to the policemen. Nor does
he think that condemning them for their mistakes
in handling a traffic snarl will benefit him or
help to solve anyone's problems.

John isn't threatened by a situation which
involves only the voice of an irate policeman
and the distant sound of automobile horns
from across the street. He points out that
Mary and he would suffer from the incident
only if they allowed it to upset them.

Does John believe that any worthwhile purpose
would be served by expressing self-righteous
indignation to the policeman?   no

Does John's attitude indicate that he would
probably refrain from reacting violently to
any external situation beyond his control?   yes

In John's opinion, any attempt by Mary to
express her indignation to the policeman
would

1. raise her tension level.

2. help the policeman to direct
   traffic.

3. teach the policeman a permanent
   lesson.

4. eliminate the traffic jam.   1

John stops at the shopping center to help
Mary select presents for some friends.
When he arrives at the office, another
writer asks him sarcastically when
everyone else will be allowed to come
to work at 10:15.

John smiles and answers that they can all
do so, as soon as they realize that they have
a right to enjoy their lives and their jobs. He
adds that they will also have to learn how to
channel their energies so that they can
accomplish a good day's work in a few hours.

The other writer's spite is swallowed up by
John's good humor. He cannot help laughing,
and has to confess that he has failed in
another attempt to "get John's goat."

In the course of John's trip to the office, it
becomes obvious that he views other drivers
as

1. fellow humans.

2. mechanized threats.

3. subhuman creatures.   1

Did John seem to be in a hurry to reach
the office?   no

John considered the policeman's tirade to be

1. a just punishment for his misdeed.

2. vicious and unwarranted.

3. unfortunate but unimportant.   3

Does John seem to feel a need to justify his
actions to policemen or colleagues?   no

CREATIVE WRITING

John has two more days to finish a project
for an electronics firm. As he works, he
sits well back in his chair, his eyes closed
and his whole body a picture of relaxation.

John dictates not only his letters and business
memoranda, but all his creative writing as
well. His words flow steadily and easily; he
seldom stops to correct a phrase. Writing
seems as natural to him as talking. He enjoys
creative work, feels no anxiety about it, and
welcomes rather than fears constructive criticism.

Do you predict that John will suffer from
rising tension as the deadline for his project   Most readers
approaches?   answered no.

After John has submitted his completed
project, will he fall prey to endless hours
of anxiety while awaiting an evaluation of   All readers
his work?   answered no.

Many executives refuse to use dictaphones,
insisting that they repeat phrases or
contradict themselves because they cannot
concentrate well enough to remember all
they have said. Must a writer who dictates
creative work be capable of relaxed
concentration?   yes

John has learned to relegate all extraneous
stimuli, such as people's voices, street
noises, and the clacking of his secretary's
typewriter, to a very low level of consciousness,
where they do not disturb his thoughts. Further-
·more, with his relaxed attitude, John isn't
plagued by tension-produced stimuli from his
own body, such as itching, restlessness, need
for a cigarette, etc.

John finds writing

1. easy.
2. difficult.   1

This results from the fact that John is

1. a great writer.
2. a hard-driving, dynamic person.
3. a brilliant thinker.
4. a relaxed, confident person.
5. a superb phrase-maker.   4

When John writes, his energy is entirely concentrated on

1. smoking and pacing the floor.
2. nervous fidgeting.
3. writing words on a pad and crossing them out.
4. creative composition.
5. rereading what he has done.
6. envisioning possible criticism.   4

A friend of yours, who speaks fluently in conversation, insists that he cannot use a dictaphone in his work. As a writer, he is probably very - tense/relaxed.   tense

In order for Barry Stone to produce his sales manual with a dictaphone, he would have to

1. become more ambitious.
2. adopt a more relaxed attitude toward his writing.
3. stop smoking.   2

ANOTHER KIND OF LUNCHEON

John has lunch with his secretary, Ruth
Barnes, and his immediate superior, Jerry
Crandall. He doesn't join them in a cocktail,
but he chats with them while they drink, looks
at the menu, and suggests possible lunches.

Does John seem to need a drink in order to
relax?   no

While conversing before lunch, John

1. gets involved in a debate.

2. stares disapprovingly at the others
    while they drink.

3. waits impatiently for the waiter.

4. enjoys looking through the menu
    and planning a good meal.   4

Ruth Barnes and Jerry Crandall take their
time with their drinks; they find that they
enjoy their cocktails more when John is
along. During the meal they talk about the
food, their hobbies, books that they are
reading, and almost anything but business.

Finally Jerry brings up the subject of John's
project. Jerry has always felt that if he
insists strongly enough, he can shorten the
time any employee takes to complete a task.
He therefore demands that John's project be
finished by the next day.

John knows that the deadline for the completion
of his work is still two days away. He therefore
replies that it will be impossible to have the
project finished by the next day, but that at his
present rate of production he will probably be
finished several hours ahead of schedule.

Jerry finds John uncooperative. John says
he is sorry Jerry feels that way, but at the
moment he himself is in the best position to
predict how long it will take to complete the
job.

John is very relaxed and courteous, but he
gives the impression that he is not going to
modify his personal orientation to conform
to someone else's standards. If Jerry
doesn't like John, or is generally dissatisfied
with his work, that is Jerry's problem, to
be resolved as he sees fit.

John's attitude shows that he is quite satisfied
with his own work, and that he has no feeling
of guilt about his performance.

Ruth finds it hard to hide a smile. John is
the only person she knows who never feels
guilty just because someone else's attitude
toward him implies that he should. She
finds him a very comfortable person to be
with; so, incidentally, does Jerry Crandall.

Without having lost any of his own dignity or
sense of security, Jerry leaves the luncheon
with renewed respect for John's integrity.

Did John enjoy his lunch?   Most readers
                                                   felt that he
                                                   probably did.

An hour later, could he tell you what he   He probably
had for lunch?   could.

Does John allow the tensions of his colleagues
to interfere with his relaxation at lunchtime?   no

Does John's relaxed attitude seem to help
others around him to relax and enjoy
themselves more?   yes

If someone like Jerry Crandall expressed
a dislike for him, John would feel that this
was

1. his secretary's problem.

2. his own problem.

3. worth evaluating, but otherwise
   entirely the other person's problem.   3

John's attitude is not simple indifference.
He examines each situation and sees whether
or not he can do something to improve it. If
action is appropriate, he takes it.   If he is
unable to help, he

1. criticizes those who are involved
   in the situation.

2. acts tired and bored.

3. applies himself to some worthwhile
   task.   3

LETTING OTHERS SPEAK

At two in the afternoon, John attends a
project directors' meeting. He is asked
to speak on the relationship of his work to
several other current publicity programs.

John knows that he is not a great speaker.
But he also knows that the success of his
talk will be measured in terms of

1. the reaction of his audience.

2. the size of his vocabulary.

3. the jokes he makes.   1

As a speaker John has two goals. His
primary objective is

1. to impress others with his
   importance.

2. to impress others with his
   brilliance.

3. to remain relaxed and comfortable
   with himself while he makes a
   presentation which satisfies his own
   standards of competence.   3

John's secondary goal is to gain acceptance
of his project and to establish its relationship
to other activities of the company. Fortunately
for John the two goals

1. coincide.

2. fail to coincide.   1

John stands in a relaxed position and speaks
in a low, pleasant voice. Would you expect
him to make flat, unqualified statements
about controversial material?   no

John admits frankly that he is simply suggesting
possibilities from his own point of view. Is this
admission likely to weaken his address?   no

Would you expect John to call on the other
project directors for suggestions?   yes

Without criticizing or distorting his colleagues'
opinions, John pulls them together into a
meaningful overall picture.

Each person in the group has several chances
to speak. As a result, all feel complimented
and enjoy the talk. By allowing others to express
their points of view, John achieves a comprehensive
presentation and learns as much as anyone present.

At the conclusion of his talk, all the project
directors praise John's work. Since they
have no first-hand knowledge of the details
of his project, it seems likely that their
favorable impressions result from

1. the high quality of John's work.

2. the way in which John presented his
    work.

3. their feeling that John is a brilliant
    person.   2

Would the speech have been as effective if
John had emphasized his own project to the
exclusion of all others?   probably not

When speaking, John concentrates on

1. establishing the importance of his
    own work.

2. projecting his emotional attitudes
    toward the subject matter.

3. remaining relaxed and developing
    his subject matter with a regard to
    the background, interests, and
    feelings of his audience.   3

It is usually easiest to win others to our
way of thinking by

1. bullying them.

2. allowing them to express their opinions
    and emphasizing the relevancy of these
    opinions to the general argument.

3. ignoring them.

4. silencing them.   2

Many speakers fail to distinguish between winning an argument and accomplishing an objective. A speaker whose attitude causes his audience to react with hostility has nothing to gain by continuing to demonstrate the correctness of his point of view in the face of increasing opposition. Although the hostility of the audience is directed primarily toward the speaker, it necessarily extends to his work.

The best course of action for a speaker faced with a hostile audience is to

1. refute every opposing point of view.

2. admit the possibility of other points of view and proceed calmly to develop the reasons for his own.

3. inform his audience that they are incapable of understanding any point of view.   2

In terms of getting things done, is there any point in demonstrating the correctness of your point of view to an audience which remains hostile to you and emotionally opposed to your work?   no

During Mr. Bigg's lecture, the members of his audience were - more/less - relaxed than   less
John's group.

They were - more/less - actively involved in   less
Mr. Bigg's presentation.

They were - more/less - hostile toward the   more
speaker than the members of John's audience.

At the conclusion of his lecture, Mr. Bigg's audience was primarily interested in

1. attacking him in any way possible.

2. praising his presentation.

3. objectively criticizing his point of view.   1

John's meeting is over at 3:15. He immediately
returns to his dictation. Today's objective is
the completion of half the work remaining on his
project. As soon as he reaches this point in the
development of his material, he stops working
and leaves for home.

In his work, John

1. tries to accomplish as much as
   possible very day.

2. sets up realistic sub-goals.

3. pursues impossibly high standards.

4. never seems to reach the goals he
   has set for himself.   2

John's early departure permits him to avoid the
rush-hour traffic. When he arrives home, he
goes for a walk with his two boys. He then lies
down and rests for fifteen minutes before dinner.

John's working day was - shorter/longer - than   shorter
Barry Stone's.

Which man accomplished more?   John

Which one seemed to expend more nervous
energy?   Barry

John/Barry - sets a definite goal for each   John
day's work and stops when he reaches it.

This leaves John with a feeling of success at
the end of the day. Does Barry have any such
feeling?   no

Does Barry seem to have any clear way of
measuring whether or not his day has been
successful?   no

RELAXING AT HOME

The Daltons take a comfortable attitude
toward dinner. They eat slowly and discuss
the events of the day. Each of the children
gets a chance to tell about his school activities.
There is no nagging, and no one is urged to eat
anything that he doesn't like.

At the end of the meal, the children go off to
do their homework. After reading the evening
paper, John spends about an hour in his
workshop, where he is currently building a
dressing table for Mary.

Later John and Mary watch television. Then
John looks over plans for building a sailboat,
reads a chapter from a book on electronics,
his newest hobby, takes a warm bath, and
prepares for bed.

Does John seem to view his life and his work
as highly competitive?   no

In the course of the day which we have just
described, did John engage in any competitive
sports or games?   no

Has he taken any heavy exercise?   no

Has he taken any mild exercise?   yes

How many walks has he taken during the day?   two

John is a - fast/slow - eater.   slow

John is able to provide a wholesome variety
of foodstuffs for his family, but he maintains
a permissive attitude with regard to the foods
which his children choose to eat.　Is this
practice likely to lead to malnutrition?　　　　　　no

John always seems to

1. be driven by deadlines.

2. be dead tired.

3. have time to do the things he enjoys.

4. race through his work and his
    leisure-time activities as fast as
    possible.

5. feel guilty about the work he should
    be doing.　　　　　　　　　　　　　　　　3

Does John watch television late into the
night?　　　　　　　　　　　　　　　　　　　no

Does he read exciting novels before going
to bed?　　　　　　　　　　　　　　　　　　no

John is in bed at 11 and sound asleep at
11:05.　Before examining the techniques
of relaxation which he uses to put himself
to sleep so easily, let's see how two of
his neighbors try to relax:

PUSHING PHONE BUTTONS

Carl Ward is a personnel consultant for an
employment agency.　When he graduated
from high school, he was voted the best-
looking boy in his class, but at 35 he
appears pudgy and middle-aged.

All day long Carl interviews applicants
and searches feverishly through his file
of job openings. On his desk a telephone
with six buttons relays frantic calls from
job candidates and prospective employers.
The flashing buttons demand his constant
attention.

Carl comes to work at nine in the morning
He seldom eats lunch or even notices when
it is noon. Often he finds that it is six or
seven in the evening before he is conscious
of the passage of time.

Carl usually arrives home at about 8 p. m.
In a final expenditure of nervous energy,
he wolfs down a large dinner without
exhibiting either appetite or enjoyment.

Feeling suddenly and completely let down,
Carl then drops into a chair in front of
his television set. He is too exhausted to
consider any other form of recreation.

Carl Ward's work day is

1. uneventful and boring.

2. frenetically active.

3. comfortably relaxed.   2

Does Carl expend great amounts of energy
in the course of his work?   yes

Does he have enough energy left to enjoy
himself after work?   no

If Carl continues his present work schedule,
we will not be surprised to learn that he

1. finds the time and energy to relax
    and enjoy himself.

2. gradually learns to make his job
    easier for himself.

3. suffers a heart attack before reaching
    the age of fifty.   3

RELAXING IN HIGH GEAR

Janet Hulme is a tired and drawn-looking
woman in her early forties. As the editor-
in-chief of a small publishing house, she
spends her working day negotiating with
authors, scanning manuscripts, dictating
reports to various company officials,
placating her art director, and arguing
with subordinate editors.

Janet proudly asserts that she is always
available for discussion of matters
pertaining to the publishing business.
She carries all her problems home, and
her phone rings far into the night.

Janet Hulme has become a processing machine,
a very active decision-making switchboard
which has to keep lighting up and making responses
because the incoming messages never stop.

Although she directs the activities of many
other people, Janet seems unable to keep
her own life under control. As a consequence,
she is

1. relaxed and rested at all times.

2. able to devote most of her life to
    enjoying herself.

3. almost completely controlled by
    external stimuli.   3

For relaxation, Janet likes to escape to
cocktail parties at the homes of friends and
business associates. These parties last far
into the night. They are often connected
with her work, and are at least as demanding
as the tasks she performs during the day.

Although both her work and her recreation
increase Janet's tension level, she sometimes
finds herself dozing off, exhausted, at her
desk or at a party.

Does Janet's present schedule give her all
the rest and relaxation she needs?   no

Since Janet prefers to resolve most problems
herself, she seldom entrusts decisions to
other people. Her consistent pursuit of this
policy results in

1. the elimination of her entire work
   load.

2. a steady reduction of her work load
   through the delegation of responsibility
   to others.

3. a constant increase in her work load.   3

Because she has so much to do, Janet cannot
devote much careful thought to individual
problems. To save time, she often makes
spur-of-the-moment decisions. In such
cases her judgment is

1. usually correct.

2. often approximate or inaccurate.   2

Instead of resolving problems, Janet's hasty
decisions only allow her to delay coming to
grips with them; in the long run such decisions

1. cost her time and decrease her efficiency.

2. save her a great deal of time.   1

Janet looks forward to her cocktail parties.
She says that she needs them in order to
"relax." Has John Dalton found more
efficient ways to relax?   yes

RECREATION VERSUS RELAXATION

As we have already remarked, many people
tend to equate recreation with relaxation.
To "relax," they change from one activity
to another. They leave their demanding
schedules in stores, schools, factories,
and offices for equally exacting routines
at parties, bars, tennis courts, pool halls,
bowling alleys, or bridge tables.

Do many people exhibit symptoms of tension
when engaged in activities normally classified
as recreation?   yes

Are some Americans' games more competitive
than their jobs?   yes

Do you know people who leave nerve-wracking
work in the competitive business world for
types of recreation which put them under even   All our readers
more stress?   answered yes.

Since we are interested in securing release
from such tension, in this course we
- will/will not - equate relaxation with   will not
participation in competitive sports.

Will we consider relaxation to be the same
as the high-tension recreation found at
parties?   no

Will we consider the intense concentration
required by hobbies such as playing poker
to be relaxation in our sense?   no

Many hobbies provide an enjoyable change
of activity. The people who pursue them
are sometimes relatively relaxed.
Nevertheless, since it is not the hobby
which causes this relaxed state, we -
will/will not - equate the pursuit of a   will not
hobby with relaxation.

On the basis of what you have learned thus
far, try to decide whether we would describe
the following activities as relaxing:

    (1) Playing on a chess team   no

    (2) Betting on horses   no

    (3) Skiing   no

    (4) Fine needle work   no

    (5) Playing tennis   no

    (6) Playing pool   no

What then, you may well ask, is defined
as relaxation? Although relaxation may
be defined in many equally acceptable
ways, our treatment of it requires a
special definition:

At the beginning of this program, we agreed
to define _____ as the absence   relaxation
of tension.

Since we are defining relaxation in terms
of its opposite, this definition won't be
completely satisfactory until we have
clearly demonstrated what we mean by
the word _____.   tension

MUSCULAR TENSION AND RELAXATION

As we have continued to use the word tension,
it has gradually taken on more and more
significance. Now let's try to develop a
precise working definition of the term.

Place your right elbow on a table or desk.
Pull your right forearm up against your
upper arm and tighten the biceps muscle as
much as you can. You should now look like
a person trying to show off his muscle.

When you tighten your biceps muscle in this
way, would you say that it is tense or relaxed?   tense

Release the tension in your biceps muscle and
let your arm drop like the empty sleeve of a
coat. Don't throw your arm down. Just let
it fall limply.

What you now feel in your right arm is the
opposite of tension. We will call this
sensation _____.   relaxation

Pull your left forearm tightly up against
your upper arm. You have now tensed
the _____ muscle of your upper left   biceps
arm as much as you can.

Relax the biceps muscle of your left arm,
letting your forearm fall.

Should you throw your arm down on the
table?   no

Throwing your arm down would involve
muscular effort. You should simply
_____ your biceps muscle and let   relax
your arm fall limply.

If you have let your forearm fall limply, like that of a rag doll, you should now have the feeling of simply "letting go" in the _____ muscle of your left arm.

biceps

The biceps muscle in your left arm is no longer tense. It is completely _____.

relaxed

Your left arm should now be lying heavily on the table. The biceps muscle should not be at all tight and swollen. The muscles of athletes are limp and formless when relaxed. Tightness in muscles which are not performing work is evidence of - relaxation/tension.

tension

What you now feel in your left arm is the opposite of tension. We define this feeling as _____.

relaxation

We tense a muscle by making an effort in order to perform work. _____ is the absence of this feeling of tension.

Relaxation

Again pull your right forearm up against your upper arm and tense your biceps muscle. The sensation which you now feel in the biceps muscle of your right arm is that of _____.

tension

Let your right forearm fall limply. The sensation in your biceps muscle is now that of _____.

relaxation

You have practiced tensing and relaxing the biceps _____ of both arms.

muscles

GENERAL AND SPECIFIC TENSION AND RELAXATION

The tensing of only one group of muscles is
referred to as <u>specific</u> tension. We refer
to the relaxing of one group of muscles as
_____ relaxation.   specific

Relaxation of all the muscles in your body is
called - specific/general - relaxation.   general

If you tense all the muscles in your body,
we say that you are in a state of -
specific/general - tension.   general

Tense all the muscles in your body as much
as you can. Your body is now in a state of
_____ tension.   general

When your muscles are tense, it is hard to
remain in one position for any length of time.
There is a natural tendency to try to relax by
moving frequently.

Tense people find it - hard/easy - to remain   hard
still.

Suppose that your neck muscles are tight and
aching from holding your head in the same
position for a long time while you read or type.
Might you be able to relieve this specific tension
by stopping and turning your head or stretching
your neck for a few minutes?   yes

Our bodies seem to try to relax tense muscle
groups by

   1. moving them.

   2. letting them remain still.   1

Therefore we think of the inability to sit still
as characteristic of - tense/relaxed - people.   tense

Many - tense/relaxed - people seem to be in   tense
constant motion.

They twitch, writhe, bite their lips, clench
their fists, scratch themselves, smoke
vigorously and endlessly, and seem unable
to sit, stand, or lie in one position for any
length of time.

Do you find it easy to remain relaxed and
motionless when you are with tense people?   probably not

But when you are with someone who is very
relaxed, you yourself probably tend to become
more _____.   relaxed

Do you enjoy yourself more when you are   All our readers
relaxed than when you are tense?   answered yes.

Remember that, for our purposes, we are
defining relaxation as the opposite of
_____.   tension

You have already experienced the sensations
of specific tension and relaxation in the biceps
_____ of both arms.   - muscles

Suppose that you were able to release the
tension in all your muscles by "letting go"
just as you did in the case of your biceps
muscles. Throughout your entire body, you
would then experience the feeling of release
that we have agreed to call _____.   relaxation

The release of tension in one set of muscles
is an example of - general/specific -   specific
relaxation.

The release of tension in all muscles of the
body is _____ relaxation.   general

If most of a person's muscles remain relaxed,
we tend to think of him as a _____ person.   relaxed

SYMPTOMS OF TENSION AND RELAXATION

Does a relaxed person move and fidget
constantly?   no

Are tense persons often fidgety?   yes

Thus we are sometimes able to recognize
the symptoms of tension in another person.

We can apply the same test to ourselves:
If you find that during your waking hours
your body is in constant motion, that you
have difficulty in going to sleep, and that
you are a light, very restless sleeper, it
is highly probable that you are a _____   tense
person.

If you have none of these symptoms, you
are probably much more relaxed than the
average person. But it is still possible
that the level of tension in your body is
high enough to make your life shorter and
less pleasant than it might otherwise be.

Decide whether a person who exhibits each of
the following symptons is tense or relaxed:

1.	cracks knuckles constantly	tense
2.	bites fingernails	tense
3.	is seldom in a hurry	relaxed
4.	hands tremble in interpersonal situations	tense
5.	sits quietly	relaxed
6.	clenches his teeth tightly and often grinds them	tense
7.	constantly fingers clothing	tense
8.	often scratches himself	tense
9.	smokes two packs of cigarettes a day	tense
10.	eats slowly	relaxed
11.	constantly handles objects in his pocket	tense
12.	bites his lips	tense
13.	consumes large quantities of alcoholic beverages	tense
14.	doesn't smoke or drink	relaxed
15.	absent-mindedly manipulates objects on a table, such as glasses, pencils, paper clips, etc.	tense
16.	constantly changes position	tense
17.	eats compulsively and constantly throughout the day	tense
18.	is an excellent listener	relaxed
19.	has severe speech difficulties in public	tense

Of course these are snap judgments. We
must exercise an element of caution. Is
it quite possible that a person who doesn't
smoke may be more tense than a chain
smoker?   yes

We ordinarily look upon the fact that a
person's body is in constant purposeless
motion as an indication that he is
- tense/relaxed.   tense

Some tense people, however, tend to hold
themselves in rigid and cramped positions.
When sitting, they may clutch the arms of
chairs or keep their hands tightly clenched
in their laps; they may tuck their feet far
back under the chair or hook them around
the chair legs.

Both excessive activity and excessive
rigidity may be symptoms of _____.   tension

SOME EXTREME CASES

Some extreme cases of psychosis might be
thought of as illustrations of how tension
can lead either to activity or to rigidity.
The hyperactivity of a manic-depressive
in his manic stage could be considered
evidence of enormous tension; the same
tension would then take the form of a sort
of rigidity in his depressed state.

Catatonic schizophrenics offer a better
example of a state of rigidity which may
result from extreme tension. Many such
patients hold themselves motionless for
long periods of time.

Fortunately, our tensions don't lead most of
us this far. But they can interfere with our
happiness and efficiency in many situations.

We have seen how – John Dalton's/Mr. Bigg's – state of tension, when speaking in public, led to continuous mechanical activity which was very annoying to his audience.

Mr. Bigg's

It was difficult for Mr. Bigg to process information and to learn in an interpersonal situation. He tended to respond to questions unthinkingly and – appropriately/inappropriately.

inappropriately

We have all known someone who is so tense that he can never get a clear look at a situation and evaluate it. Such a person usually seems to answer questions

1. appropriately.

2. off the top of his head.

3. after mature consideration.

2

Tense people's answers are usually inappropriate to the situations in which they find themselves. They reply in terms of

1. their carefully thought out personal objectives.

2. their plans for the future.

3. their automatic reactions to the most recent stimulus.

3

After a person has left a tension-producing situation, he can think of all the remarks he should have made. He usually considers this tardy verbal facility to be the product of mature reflection. The fact is that he is able to find the appropriate response as soon as he becomes - tense/relaxed.

relaxed

All tense people feel awkward. Some try to mask their nervousness by constant speech and movement. We say that they manifest their tension by - rigidity/hyperactivity.

hyperactivity

Other tense people devote all their energy to maintaining one physical position, for fear that any gesture will be ungainly or wrong. When they are forced to change position, their tension inhibits free muscular action, and their movements seem very - clumsy/graceful.

clumsy

DANCING SCHOOL

Mr. Bigg's daughter Susan and Barry Stone's
son Jack are junior high school students. From
what we know of their home environments, we
would surmise that they tend to be - tense/relaxed -   tense
in social situations.

Let's look at Susan and Jack during their
first evening at dancing school:

Jack sits waiting for the dreaded moment when
he must first step out on the dance floor. He
crouches forward, his legs as stiff as boards,
his hands clutched tightly in his lap, and his
elbows pressing into the arms of the chair.

Jack wears a ferocious scowl, calculated to
express disdain and superiority. He swallows
constantly and his breathing is rapid and shallow.

Jack's response to a tension-producing situation
is - rigidity/hyperactivity.   rigidity

On the other side of the room, Susan Bigg is
speaking rapidly to several of her girl friends,
who seem to be trying to imitate Jack's posture
and poise. Susan herself is a picture of animation.
She rattles on from topic to topic, but her remarks
seem to have little relation to the situation in which
she finds herself.

Does tension make Susan as rigid as Jack?   no

Her response is hyper_____.   hyper<u>activity</u>

Finally the teacher comes over and asks Susan
if she would like to dance. Susan says, "Oh,
I'd just love to, " and remains seated. The
dancing teacher then points out that if Susan is
going to dance, she will have to stand up.

Susan says, "Oh, I see. I mean, I thought you
meant. . . that is, I thought you were asking
whether I liked to dance in general. . . I didn't
know you meant that I should dance right this
minute. "

Susan springs to her feet much too suddenly,
and her purse clatters from her lap to the
floor. Bending down to pick up her purse,
she manages to bump both the chair and
the dancing teacher. She tries to cover her
embarrassment with a stream of disconnected
remarks.

Tense people tend to react - appropriately/
inappropriately.

inappropriately

Meanwhile, the other dancing instructor has
collared Jack and is steering him precariously
across the floor toward Susan.

Jack's leg muscles are so tense that he seems
barely able to maintain his balance. Several
times he skids dangerously on the polished
floor. Finally he arrives, red-faced, and
gasps out the newly memorized, "Would-you-
care-to-dance?"

Susan has completely forgotten what she is
supposed to say. She replies, "Oh, I don't
mind. . . I mean, I guess so. . . I mean,
that is, if you really want to. . . I mean,
why not?" and drops her purse again.

People who are very conscious of others'
opinions tend to be - tense/relaxed.

tense

When Jack and Susan finally start to dance,
Jack strides rigidly and mechanically about
the floor in a stiff-legged rhythm of his own,
while Susan hops and jiggles at about twice
the tempo of the music.

Susan and Jack dance - gracefully/awkwardly.

awkwardly

Their actions seem to be governed largely by

1. their interest in dancing.

2. their interest in each other.

3. their inner tensions.

4. their desire to enjoy themselves.   3

Even while we smile at the terrors and
mistakes of Susan and Jack, we may be
hiding similar tensions from ourselves.
This is one reason why it is such good
practice for us to observe others. We
can see that people who move slowly,
easily, and gracefully are usually -
tense/relaxed.   relaxed

We notice that people whose movements
are rapid and jerky, or stiff, awkward,
and cramped, are generally _____.   tense

This suggests a way for us to achieve
relaxation. We might try imitating relaxed
people by reminding ourselves to move
slowly, rhythmically, and gracefully.

This approach offers us a good point of
departure, but in actual practice it is too
difficult for most people. However much
a person may remind himself to imitate his
more relaxed friends, the habits of tension
remain too deeply ingrained. Except for
occasional moments of insight, he will
continue to act much as he did before.

Let's observe a few more people, with a
view to finding an effective path to relaxation:

You see a man stretching and yawning. At
that moment would you describe him as
tense or relaxed?   relaxed

Think of a woman you know who frowns constantly.
Now review her other characteristics in the light
of what you have read in this program. Do you
find that she is a relaxed person?   probably not

Think of another friend who always wears an
easy smile. Do her other characteristics
indicate that she is a relatively relaxed person?   They probably do.

You see a woman with her eyes closed, leaning
back comfortably in a chair. Her attitude
indicates a state of - tension/relaxation.   relaxation

APPLYING WHAT WE HAVE LEARNED

Since it's easier to observe symptoms of
tension in others than in ourselves, we have
been describing the external characteristics
of various people who might be considered
tense or relaxed.

You are now familar with a number of
manifestations of tension. You know what
sort of behavior you wish to avoid and why
it is undesirable. You will now learn how
to avoid it by gaining control of your body
so that you can relax at will.

Recall the way in which you learned to tense
and relax the biceps-muscle of either arm.
Was this an example of general relaxation?   no

It was an example of _____ relaxation.   specific

The voluntary muscles are those which are
under our conscious control. Whenever we
speak of muscles in this course, we will
always mean _____ muscles.   voluntary

General relaxation consists of releasing the
tension in all groups of voluntary _____   muscles
in the body.

You can achieve general relaxation in several
ways. One way involves specifically relaxing
each individual muscle group in the body. When
all these muscle groups have been relaxed, you
will have achieved _____ relaxation.   general

You can start at the feet and specifically relax
each group of muscles in turn until you reach
the scalp muscles at the other end of the body.

Before we begin the study of this step-by-step
process, let's consider some easier ways to
approach the state of relaxation. We have
already seen that smiling, yawning, and
stretching are among the external manifestations
of - tension/relaxation.   relaxation

If the process is reversible, this suggests
three possible ways to achieve some measure
of general relaxation. You might _____,   smile
_____ or _____.   yawn, stretch

This approach may seem odd to you at first.
Perhaps you have always believed that your
moods controlled the ways in which your body
manifested them.

You might agree that relaxed people tend to
smile often, but you might question the
statement that people who smile tend to be
more relaxed. It is, however, the opinion
of many specialists that smiling does contribute
to _____.   relaxation

Most of us are accustomed to thinking in quite
different terms. We normally say that we
laugh because we are amused. But we might
also say that we are amused because we
_____.   laugh

Similarly, rather than saying that we cry
because we are sad, we might say that we
are sad because we _____.   cry

According to the famous psychologist and
philosopher, William James, instead of
saying that we run because we are afraid,
it might make more sense to say that we
are _____ because we _____.   afraid, run

People who espouse this point of view believe
that we share in the "emotional" reactions of
our bodies when these reactions are "telegraphed"
to our brains.

This might be explained in terms of a feed-back
mechanism: If enjoyment causes us to smile or
amusement makes us laugh, the reaction of
smiling or laughing feeds back to the central
nervous system and contributes to a stronger
tendency to smile or laugh.

In other words, when things which amuse you
cause you to laugh, the laughter itself feeds
back and tends to heighten your sense of
amusement.

If all this is true, we may be able to modify
unwanted reaction. We seem to have
some control over our bodies. Can you,
for example, smile, stretch, or yawn
whenever you wish?

All readers
answered <u>yes</u>.

Is laughter incompatible with the muscular
tensions of such emotional reactions as
frowning or sneering?

yes

We can take advantage of the fact that tension
and relaxation are mutually exclusive
activities for the same muscle groups.
That is to say, tension and relaxation are
- compatible/incompatible.

incompatible

Can the same group of muscles be both
tense and relaxed at the same time?

no

Keeping this in mind, let's try a simple
experiment. Try to tense all your muscles
as much as possible. Your body should now
be in a state of general _____.

tension

Now laugh. Do you find it almost impossible
to remain tense while laughing?

Most readers
answered <u>yes</u>.

Again tense all the muscles in your body as
much as possible. Now stretch. Can you
maintain tension in the muscles which are
engaged in stretching?

no

Tense your body again. Yawn. While yawning,
you find it easy/hard - to maintain the tension
in your muscles.

hard

We have spoken of smiling, yawning, and
stretching as three good aids to general
relaxation. Of these three, the most
socially acceptable is _____.

smiling

Which is the easiest to maintain over a
prolonged period of time?

smiling

What two aids to general relaxation are
preferably practiced in private?

yawning
stretching

These considerations indicate that the one aid
to relaxation which we can practice in almost
any situation is the _____.

smile

MEETING "TENSE SITUATIONS"

The facial muscles, which are necessarily
relaxed when you are smiling, are among
the most important in the body in terms of
tension and relaxation. What might be a
good piece of initial advice to a person
about to enter into a "tense situation"?

Smile!

Of course there is really no such thing as
a "tense situation." In the sense in which
we are using the word in this program,
tension can exist only

1. in the outside world.

2. in our bodies.

2

But there are situations in which many
people customarily grow tense. The type
of situation which leads to tension and the
amount of tension caused vary from
individual to individual.

We have mentioned three aids to general
relaxation. Two of these are better
practiced before you enter into a type of
situation which previously made you tense.
These are _____ and _____.

yawning
stretching

The aid to relaxation which can be maintained
over periods of time is the _____.

smile

Suppose that you are about to enter into the
following situation:

You are to give a talk before a hostile and
critical group. Under such circumstances,
many speakers become tense and hostile
themselves and make a very bad impression
on the audience. You might take a step
toward avoiding this by deciding to keep the
suggestion of a _____ playing about your
lips during your address.

smile

If before you face your audience you can find
a moment when you are unobserved, you might
try a good stretch and _____.

yawn

A tense speaker appears hostile; his audience
is automatically prepared to react unfavorably
and to interpret his words as threats.   A
smiling person doesn't project hostility; he
doesn't seem prepared to antagonize people by
tensely seeking out problems or fights.   A
smile serves to relax

    1. only the speaker.

    2. only the audience.

    3. neither the speaker nor the audience.

    4. both the speaker and the audience.   4

Tension and relaxation are immediately and
powerfully communicated.   As we have already
indicated, this suggests another way to relax:

Seek the society of _____ people and   relaxed
avoid _____ people.   tense

When you are first learning how to relax, you
will find that you make better progress if you
associate only with _____ people.   relaxed

If your job forces you to deal with tense people,
you can help them and yourself by maintaining
a relaxed attitude.   An easy smile from you
will tend to bring answering smiles which will
relax your companions.

At first you will find it very hard to relax in
situations which have previously caused you
considerable tension.   The experience of
many people indicates that it is helpful to
place small cards reading "relax" in your
wallet, your desk drawers, and other places
where you are likely to see them at odd
moments during the day.

Initially the cards will be more useful if you
also write on them the following three aids
to general relaxation:

                                              smile, yawn

_____, _____, _____   stretch

WINNING ARGUMENTS AND LOSING PATIENTS

Dr. Harris is a specialist in a large clinic.
He spends a good part of his day dealing
with difficult cases which have been referred
to him by other doctors. By the time he sees
these patients, they have often been enraged
by a series of frustrating experiences. They
tend to vent their hostility on him.

Formerly Dr. Harris made it a practice to
interrupt such patients in the middle of their
complaints. He then explained that he was a
leading specialist who was donating his time
and services to help them. He added that he
was under no obligation to listen to their
emotional outbursts; if they didn't appreciate
his efforts, they were at liberty to go elsewhere.

In other words, the doctor became almost as
tense as his patients, and answered their
complaints with tirades of his own. He
devoted considerable time to thinking up
clever retorts, and he won many arguments,
but he found that this approach to the situation
only made him very unhappy in his chosen work.

Recently Dr. Harris has been using a new
technique. He receives each patient with an
easy smile on his face, and maintains the
smile while the patient "has his say."

Dr. Harris doesn't reply to the torrent of
complaints. He waits until the patient has
finished, and then says, "Well, it seems
that you've been having a bad time. Let's
see if I can help you." He then proceeds
with his own examination and diagnosis.
Would you suspect that he now has more
contrite and cooperative patients?

He says that
this is almost
invariably true

Dr. Harris has come to realize that his
patients weren't really attacking him.
They were unleashing their frustrations
on him because he was the only available
representative of a profession which they
felt had treated them shabbily. When he
tried to think of the most incisive replies,
he was giving the patients exactly what they
wanted. They felt a need to communicate
their unhappiness to him. His angry
answers proved that they had accomplished
the following two things:

(1) They had proved the importance of
themselves and their problems by
getting him to respond either
defensively or aggressively.

(2) They had brought him down to their
own level by making him respond in
the same angry, irrational way that
they were acting.

Thus we see that the doctor's need to "talk
back" to his patients represented his

1.   triumph over himself.

2.   triumph over his patients.

3.   failure to control himself.   3

Dr. Harris's original hostile attitude toward
his patients made it - easier/harder - for   harder
him to treat them effectively.

Whenever you devote your time to thinking
up scathing remarks, you are

1.   thinking only of your own happiness.

2.   concerned with the happiness of others.

3.   thinking only of looking important in
other people's eyes.   3

The whole concept of the "perfect squelch"
involves a serious contradiction. When
you indulge in cutting remarks, you are
hoping to demonstrate your superiority to
the very person you are insulting. But
even as you attack him, you seem to seek
compliments on your brilliance. Is such
a display likely to leave him with a favorable
impression of you?   no

PLEASE DON'T BITE THE DENTIST

Dentists tend to have difficult patients.
People who don't grow tense in a dentist's
office are - common/relatively rare.   relatively rare

If the dentist himself shows signs of irritation,
he can make the patient's situation almost
unendurable.

Over a period of time, most dentists learn
to adopt a relaxed and comforting manner.
Those who exhibit signs of nervousness and
strain have fewer patients.

Dental patients have even greater need of
relaxation than the dentists themselves. At
this point you may object that such techniques
as smiling, yawning and stretching aren't
easy to practice with a drill in your mouth.

But you can practice these aids to general
_____ before you sit in the   relaxation
dentist's chair. They will reduce much of
the anxiety which you feel while you wait for
the dental work to begin.

And there are other techniques of general
relaxation which can be used even by a person
in the dentist's chair. The simplest of these
consists merely in closing your eyes.

Will this eliminate many of the tension-
producing stimuli provided by the room
and the dental instruments?   yes

Furthermore, you tend to associate the
act of closing your eyes with relaxation.
Ordinarily you close your eyes only when
you are in a situation in which you feel
sure that you - will/will not - be hurt.   will not

Thus the reassuring nature of this act
helps to relax you, because you associate
it only with

    1.   situations in which you are normally
       relaxed.

    2.   tension-producing situations.   1

We have just discussed an aid to general
relaxation which is applicable in most
situations and particularly useful in the
dentist's chair. Rather than watch the
dentist prepare his drills, hypodermics,
forceps, etc., you simply ....   close your eyes
              (Finish the sentence.)

Whenever possible, this technique should be
used in conjunction with other aids to
_____ because it eliminates many   relaxation
of the visual stimuli which produce tension.

If you are seated with a number of people who
are tensely waiting for a late plane, you can
isolate yourself from the group and their   closing your
problems by ....   eyes
        (Finish the sentence.)

We will soon see how a process of step-by-step
relaxation can be used even more effectively in
such instances.

For the moment, we will simply add another
aid to general relaxation which can also be
used even in the dentist's chair: this consists
of taking slow, deep breaths.

Shallow, rapid breathing is characteristic of
a - tense/relaxed - person.   tense

Are panting and gasping for breath thought of
as common symptoms of distress and anxiety?   yes

We associate slow, deep breathing with situations   free from
in which we are - anxious/free from anxiety.   anxiety

Give two aids to general relaxation which may   closing your eyes
be employed even in the dentist's chair.   taking slow,
                                                     deep breaths

In the dentist's chair, or in any tense situation
where passive waiting is required, once you
have relaxed sufficiently to gain control of your
thoughts, concentrate on something very pleasant
which is far removed from your situation, or
select a problem which requires all your mental
concentration. This will serve to keep you from
dwelling on your ordeal.

Some people are sure that it is their duty to
worry about friends and relatives who are in
dangerous situations. They say that they would
feel guilty if they didn't think of their loved ones
constantly. Can you really help anyone else by
worrying about situations over which you have no
control?   no

TAKING TESTS

Largely as a result of our school experiences,
most of us become tense at the thought of taking
a test. Some people are incapable of facing a
situation in which they feel that they are being
tested. Even very simple tests can occasion
strong feelings of tension and anxiety.

The test or retest for a driver's license is
a particularly difficult situation for adults.
They must remember a series of facts, and
their coordination must remain unaffected
by tension. Which of the following aids to
general relaxation might you use while actually
driving in the test situation?

smiling

smiling

stretching

yawning

closing your eyes

taking slow, deep breaths

taking slow,
deep breaths

Would the other three techniques be useful
before and after taking the driving test?

yes

THE POWER OF A WORD

We have considered five ways of achieving
general _____.

relaxation

A sixth aid to general relaxation consists
simply of telling yourself to relax.   The
word relax becomes much more effective
after you have experienced the sensation
of relaxation which the other techniques
bring. Repeat the word "relax" several
times. You will feel how some of the
tension leaves the muscles in your body.
Do you find yourself more relaxed than
you were before reading this paragraph?

All readers
answered yes.

The repetition of the word _____ is
our sixth aid to general relaxation.

relax

Name the six aids to general relaxation which we have employed.

smiling
yawning
stretching
closing your eyes
slow, deep
breathing
repetition of
the word <u>relax</u>

All these techniques represent relatively simple ways to induce _____ relaxation.

general

As we have already indicated, there is a much more effective, step-by-step method of accomplishing this objective: This is the progressive, specific relaxation of each individual group of voluntary _____ in the body.

muscles

After you have practiced progressive relaxation for several weeks, and have experienced much deeper states of relaxation, you will find that the other six techniques also become much - more/less - effective.

more

The word "relax," for example, will have far - greater/less - meaning for you.

greater

MORE PRACTICE IN SPECIFIC RELAXATION

Specific relaxation is concerned with

1. specific situations.
2. individual muscles and muscle groups.
3. the entire body.

2

Our initial practice in _____ relaxation consisted of learning to relax the biceps muscles of the upper arms.

specific

If possible, you should lie in bed while reading
the following frames. You will thus be able to
practice the exercises which they contain. Prop
yourself up with pillows so that you can read
comfortably.

If it is impossible for you to lie down while you
read this, simply assume the most comfortable
position you can, and practice as many of the
exercises as your environment will permit.

For a start, repeat the exercise of tensing the
biceps muscle of your right arm. Pull your
right forearm against your upper arm and
tighten the biceps muscle as much as you can.

Your biceps muscle is now tight and swollen.
We have defined the sensation which you
experience as _____.   tension

Relax your biceps muscle completely, letting
your right forearm fall limply on the bed.

The sensation which you now feel in your biceps
muscle is defined as _____.   relaxation

Relaxation is the absence of the feeling of
_____.   tension

Pull your left forearm against your upper arm
and tighten the biceps muscle as much as you
can. Note the sensation of _____ which   tension
you feel in the muscle.

Let your left forearm fall limply on the bed.
You have relaxed the tension in the biceps
muscle of your left arm. The sensation which
you now feel in that muscle is the absence of
tension, which we have agreed to define as
_____.   relaxation

You will now practice relaxing each set of
voluntary muscles in your body, just as you
relaxed the biceps muscles of both arms.
These exercises will give you conscious
control over the specific relaxation of each
group of _____.   muscles

In this way you will learn to detect and
eliminate the tensions in your body. Until
now you have been unaware of these tensions.
They have remained on an unconscious level.
Now you will establish - conscious/unconscious -   conscious
control over them.

This will give you a heightened awareness of
the state of your muscles and a greater control
over your entire body.

Still lying in the same position on the bed, raise
your right leg, without bending the knee, until
your heel is about two feet above the bed.

The muscles in your upper right leg are being
used to hold it above the bed.   These muscles
are - tense/relaxed.   tense

Now relax the muscles of your upper right leg
so that the leg falls heavily to the bed.

Did you throw your leg down on the bed?   Your answer
                                                 should be no.

Would throwing your leg down on the bed
involve exertion and muscular tension?   yes

You should have let your leg fall limply as
if it were the leg of a rag doll. What you
now feel in your right leg is the absence of
effort and tension. Your right leg is no longer
_____; it is _____.   tense, relaxed

Remember that we are defining relaxation in
terms of the absence of _____.   tension

Now raise your left leg until your heel is about
two feet above the bed. Are the muscles of your
upper left leg very tense?   yes

Let your left leg fall to the bed. The upper leg
muscles are now _____.   relaxed

REVIEW

Decide whether each of the following
statements are true or false:

1. When you tense and relax a particular
group of muscles, you are practicing
<u>general</u> relaxation.   false

2. <u>Specific</u> relaxation consists of relaxing
your entire body.   false

3. We define relaxation as the absence of
the sensation of tension.   true

4. When you relax the muscles which have
been holding your leg up and away from
the bed, you should have the sensation
of throwing your leg down on the bed.   false

5. A feeling of limpness in a group of
muscles is a sign of relaxation.   true

SPECIFIC TENSION VERSUS SPECIFIC RELAXATION

With your arms still lying flat at your sides,
make a fist with your right hand and clench
it as tightly as you can. This fist should now
be very - tense/relaxed.   tense

Open your fist and let your right hand rest
palm downward on the bed. All the fingers
of this hand should now be relaxed. Do you   You don't if the
feel any tendency for your right hand to strain   hand is completely
upward and away from the bed?   relaxed.

Clench your left fist as tightly as you can.
Your left hand is now _____, but your   tense
right hand remains _____.   relaxed

This is a good example of specific tension and
specific relaxation. Can one part of your body
be tense while another part is relaxed?   yes

This sort of exercise is very useful. Eventually
it will permit you to establish a precise control
over the various parts of your body.

Will you then be able to let some muscle
groups relax while others work?   yes

A control of the amount of specific tension
introduced into your body is important in
working situations where complete general
relaxation is - possible/impossible.   impossible

Your goal in such a situation will be to
approximate general relaxation as closely
as your work permits. Thus you will try
to relax

    1. all your muscle groups.

    2. the muscles which you need
       to perform your work.

    3. all muscle groups except those which
       you need to perform a given task.   3

The strict localization of _____ tension   specific
greatly reduces your anxiety and your output
of nervous energy. Mastery of this technique
will permit you to work long hours very
comfortably and effectively.

Somewhat later we will practice approximating
general relaxation in a number of situations
involving _____ tension.   specific

For the time being, simply remember that
when you are working you should strive to

    1. tense only the muscles necessary to
       perform a specific task.

    2. avoid all tension forever.

    3. remain as tense as possible in order
       to work more effectively.   1

DETECTING HIDDEN TENSIONS

Thus far we have been tensing muscle groups
by making them perform work. They have
been used to move an arm, a leg or a hand.

You will find that it is comparatively easy to
detect the sensation of tension in a muscle
when you contract it to move some part of
your body. We will speak of this sensation
as <u>overt</u> _____.   tension

Tension is much harder to detect when no
effort is being made and the muscles of your
body remain motionless. We will call this
sensation <u>hidden</u> _____.   tension

With your arms at your sides and both hands
lying palm downward on the bed, tense your
right hand as much as possible. This time
don't clench it into a fist. In fact, don't move
the hand at all; leave it in the same position,
palm downward on the bed. But strain to make
your hand and fingers as tense as possible.

Are both your hands still lying in the same
position?   yes

Your left hand is - tense/relaxed.   relaxed

Your right hand is _____.   tense

Your relaxed left hand continues to lie limply
and heavily on the bed. Notice that your
tense right hand seems to be trying to hold
itself up off the bed.

The tendency to strain up and away from the
bed is characteristic of - tension/relaxation.   tension

Relax your right hand. It should seem to lie
heavily against the bed without your having
made any effort to push it down. Both hands
should now be lying relaxed, palm downward,
on the bed.

Without moving your left hand, tense it as much
as possible. You should feel it straining as if it
were trying to move - toward/away from - the   away from
bed.

The sensation which you feel when you use your
biceps to move your right forearm is called
- overt/hidden - tension.   overt

The sensation which you feel in a muscle group
which is lying motionless but nevertheless seems
to be straining up and away from the bed is called
_____ tension.   hidden

Relax both hands as much as possible. In your
hands you should now feel the absence of tension
which we have agreed to call _____.   relaxation

Can muscles be tense even when you are not
using them to move parts of your body?   yes

Have you tensed and relaxed both hands without
moving them from their positions on the bed?   yes

Tense your right forearm. You should feel it
strain as if trying to move - toward/away from -   away from
the bed.

Relax your right forearm. Does it now seem to
lie limply against the bed?   It should.

Let's summarize by saying that when you are
lying down, the tendency of a part of your body
to strain as if trying to move away from the
bed is characteristic of hidden _____.

tension

Those parts of your body which lie limply and
heavily against the bed are much more

_____.

relaxed

Tense your right lower leg. It will strain as
if trying to move ················
              (in what direction)

away from
the bed

Relax your right lower leg. It will lie limply
and heavily ··················

against the bed

Tense your left lower leg. It will strain as
if ·······························

trying to move
away from the
bed

Relax your left lower leg. How should it
seem to lie?

limply and
heavily against
the bed

Whenever you tense a group of muscles
controlling a part of your body which is in
contact with the bed, that part of your body
seems to strain ···············
              (in what direction)

away from
the bed

Whenever you relax these same muscles,
the part of the body in which they are found
will seem to lie ························
              (how)

limply and
heavily against
the bed

Tense your right foot as much as possible.
Do you feel it moving away from the bed?

You should.

Relax your right foot. Does it now seem to
lie limply and heavily against the bed?

It should.

Tense your left foot. What happens?	It strains up and away from the bed.
Relax your left foot. What happens?	It lies limply and heavily against the bed.
Tense the muscles of your neck. Do they strain as if trying to hold your head and neck up and away from the supporting pillows?	yes
Relax your neck muscles. Your head and neck seem to - move away from/fall back against - the pillows.	fall back against
Tense the muscles of your lower back. Your back strains	upward and away from the bed

Tense the muscles of your upper back. You should feel as though you are trying to hold yourself up off the pillows and the bed.

Relax your back muscles. Do you feel as if you are falling back against the pillows and the bed?   You should.

Decide whether each of the following is an example of <u>overt</u> tension or <u>hidden</u> tension:

1. You use your biceps muscle to pull your right forearm up against your upper arm.   overt

2. You clench your left hand into a tight fist.   overt

3. You feel as if your neck muscles are straining upward and away from the bed.   hidden

4. You have placed your right hand palm downward on the bed, but it doesn't feel limp and heavy.   hidden

5. You use your neck muscles to raise your head three inches from the bed.   overt

MORE TRAINING IN RELEASING TENSION

Tense all the muscles of your body as much as
you can. You should feel as if your muscles
are trying to lift your entire body off the bed.
Your body is in a state of - general/specific -   general
tension.

Do you think that you could go to sleep while
maintaining your muscles in this state of   All our readers
tension?   said <u>no</u>.

Repeat the word "relax, " and release the tension
in your body as much as possible. Some hidden
tension will remain in each muscle group.   Try
to release this tension by repeating the words
"let go" several times.

Lift your right leg and foot up from the bed.   A
certain amount of effort is required to move part
of your body in this way.   Do groups of muscles
in your right leg become tense?   yes

Since the rest of your body has remained relaxed,
this is an example of - general/specific - tension.   specific

We have already discussed the fact that exercises
which involve tensing some parts of your body,
while letting others remain relaxed, will eventually
help you to - sleep/work - more effectively.   work

You have learned to recognize the sensation of
tension in groups of moving muscles.   We have
agreed to call this _____ tension.   overt

Have you also found that you can recognize
tension in groups of muscles which are not
moving or causing other parts of your body
to move?   yes

Did these apparently motionless muscle groups give the impression of trying to strain upward and away from the bed?   yes

We define the sensation which you felt in these <u>motionless</u> muscle groups as _____ tension.   hidden

In several groups of muscles you have learned to recognize the total absence of effort, strain, or tension, which we call _____.   relaxation

Thus far we have consistently defined relaxation in negative terms. It is the opposite or absence of _____.   tension

You can feel relaxation only as a lack of tension in your muscles. Therefore you must learn to recognize tension and to eliminate it in order to have the sensation of _____.   relaxation

MORE HIDDEN TENSIONS

We will now learn to recognize hidden tensions in new groups of muscles. These muscles will neither try to move parts of your body nor will they be in contact with the bed. As a consequence you - will/won't - be able to feel them strain   won't
upward and away from the bed when they are tense.

Let's start by tensing the muscles of your scalp. You will not feel your head pulled up and away from the pillow, but you will notice a definite tugging sensation at your forehead and at the sides of your head. This is the feeling of _____ in your scalp.   tension

Relax your scalp. Does the tugging sensation
in your forehead and at the sides of your head
disappear?   It should.

Tense the muscles of your stomach. The
tugging sensation should now be felt near your
hip bones and lower ribs.

Relax your stomach muscles. The tugging
sensation should disappear. Practice this
several times until you feel that you can
recognize the sensation easily.

You recognize the feeling of _____   relaxation
in your scalp or stomach muscles by the
absence of any pulling sensation.

Now tense the muscles of your face. Do you   If not, keep
feel the pulling or tugging sensation at your   tensing your
ears and around your mouth?   facial muscles
                                                     until you do.

Relax the muscles of your face. The tugging
sensation should disappear. Practice several
more times.

The feeling of tension in your facial muscles
can be identified by a tugging sensation at your
ears and around your _____.   mouth

You can eliminate this sensation and the tension
which accompanies it by _____ the   relaxing
muscles of your face.

Does creasing your forehead into a deep frown
also involve tensing some of your facial muscles?   yes

A SMALL BUT IMPORTANT MUSCLE GROUP

We will now practice tensing and relaxing a very
important group of muscles.

Clench your jaw tightly and tense the muscles of
your mouth and tongue. Feel the pressure of your
lips and the way in which your tongue seems to
push upward against the roof of your mouth.

This is the feeling of _____ in the   tension
muscles of your mouth.

Now let your jaw sag and relax the muscles of
your mouth and tongue. Your mouth should
feel just ready to open, with your lips barely
touching each other and your tongue seeming
to float. This is the sensation of _____   relaxation
in the muscles of your mouth.

You have just learned how to relax the muscles
of your _____. Practice tensing and   mouth
relaxing these muscles several more times.

THE MOST IMPORTANT MUSCLE GROUP

We have saved for the very last the muscles of
the eyes. For our purposes these are the most
important muscles and the most difficult to relax.

Hold this book close to your face and stare hard
at the underlined word TENSION. You should
feel the tensing of your _____ muscles as a   eye
sensation of strain in your eyelids.

Hold the book away and let your eye muscles
relax. You should have a sensation of "letting
go" similar to that which you felt when you
relaxed your biceps muscle and let your forearm
fall against the bed.

Imagine that your eyes are loose in their
sockets and about to fall out. The sensation
of release which you now feel in your eyes
is that of _____.   relaxation

If your goal is complete general relaxation,
the most important specific muscles for you
to relax are those of your _____.   eyes

Second in importance are the muscles of your
mouth.

Because of the feedback mechanism which we
have already mentioned, all muscle groups in
your body interact. Will the specific relaxation
of any muscle group reduce the state of general
tension in your body to some extent?   yes

But some groups of muscles make a much
greater contribution than others. Would you
expect the relaxation of your thumbs to be as
important as that of your eyes?   no

In terms of relaxation, rank the following
groups of muscles in order of importance,
starting with the most important:

_____   muscles of the arms   3

_____   muscles of the mouth   2

_____   muscles of the eyes   1

If you relax the muscles of your eyes and
mouth completely, it is almost impossible
to maintain a state of general _____   tension
throughout the rest of your body.

We have already made use of this interesting
fact in the techniques employed to achieve
general relaxation. Was smiling one of these
techniques?   yes

Smiling is an excellent way to relax the
muscles of your eyes and mouth. Try
smiling now. Do your feel your eyes and   All readers
mouth starting to relax?   answered <u>yes</u>.

The greatest contribution to general relaxation
is made by the muscles of the _____ and   eyes
_____.   mouth

If you specifically relax the muscles of your
eyes and mouth, you have made a great step
toward the _____ relaxation of your   general
entire body.

LOOKING BACKWARD

Let's pause for a moment and consider the
progress you have made.

You are familiar with the sensations of
_____ and relaxation, and with   tension
various ways of causing these sensations.

Tension can be caused by moving muscles
or by simply tightening them. When movement
is involved, tension is - hard/easy - to   easy
recognize.

The sensation in muscles which are moving
or causing parts of your body to move is
called _____ tension.   overt

Even when your body is apparently motionless,
some groups of muscles may be straining upward
and away from their points of support. The
sensation in these muscles is that of _____   hidden
tension.

It is hardest to recognize hidden tension in muscle groups located in parts of the body which - are/aren't - in contact with points of support.

aren't

In learning to relax such groups of muscles, we first tense them; when we release the tension, we have the sensation of its absence which we have agreed to call _____.

relaxation

You are now able to recognize even small amounts of hidden tension in your muscles. Soon you will use this ability to develop some techniques for putting yourself to sleep.

Some people fall asleep quickly because they habitually drive themselves to the point of exhaustion. If you are such a person, it's quite possible that you are getting too little rest. Even while you are asleep, hidden tensions may remain in your muscles.

Whether you have ever been troubled by insomnia or not, learning to fall into a deep, relaxed sleep whenever you wish can be of great benefit to you. During the day it will allow you to take short naps which will rest you thoroughly and permit you to work with renewed efficiency on awakening.

Would you suspect that some of the techniques which put you to sleep might also be useful during your waking hours?

If you did suspect this, you would be quite correct.

HOW TO STAY AWAKE

Before we discuss the relationship between relaxation and sleep, we need to look at some routines which prevent many people from relaxing.

An examination of behavior patterns of insomniacs often reveals that they prepare for sleep in ways which would suffice to keep a log awake. They may be very intelligent people, but force of habit prevents them from seeing their mistakes.

See if you can find the fallacies in the following ways of preparing for sleep:

EATING AND DRINKING HABITS

Mary always drinks two cups of coffee just before going to bed.

Coffee contains caffein. Any stimulant is an enemy of relaxation and sleep.

Jane avoids coffee because she knows that it contains caffein. She usually drinks several cups of tea before retiring.

Tea also contains caffein.

Harriet knows that she should avoid coffee and tea. She loves cola drinks of all kinds and always has one at bedtime.

Some cola drinks contain caffein.

Jack's doctor has ordered him to avoid stimulants before retiring. He suggested that Jack take a glass of warm milk instead of his regular cup of coffee. Jack has developed a great taste for milk; he now drinks a quart of it every night before he goes to bed.

Jack should restrict his intake of liquids after dinnertime. Few people can sleep with a full bladder.

George suffers from attacks of acute indigestion. For some years he worked in Madrid, where he habitually dined at 10:30 in the evening. Since his present job often keeps him in the office until late in the evening, he has continued this practice. He goes to bed almost immediately after dinner, but has difficulty in falling asleep.

It is hard for many people to sleep with a full stomach. For a person who suffers from indigestion it is almost impossible.

HEALTHFUL EXERCISE

Jim hates exercise and studiously avoids physical effort of any kind. At night he lies down mentally exhausted by a series of emotional strains but very much awake physically.

Jim's body does not feel that it needs sleep. Moderate daily exercise is a requirement for sound sleep.

Bill is a young man whose doctor recommended that he take more physical exercise. Every night he runs a quarter of a mile just before going to bed.

Just after heavy exercise the heart is beating very fast and there is considerable residual tension in the muscles. It takes a long time for the body to relax sufficiently for sleep.

Harry also exercises just before going to bed. Since he knows that he shouldn't indulge in strenuous exercise at this time, he limits himself to calisthenics, stretching exercises, and lifting light weights. But it still takes him a long time to go to sleep.

These are excellent exercises which do not place as much strain on the heart as running for long distances. But they still increase the speed of the heartbeat and leave the muscles so tense that it is difficult to fall asleep.

Mary always goes for a long walk just before going to bed.

Most people should take even as mild an exercise as walking at least one hour before retiring.

Moderate open-air exercise such as walking is good for all of us. It tires muscles without exhausting them and helps the appetite. Does it tend to rev up the human machine as much as more violent exercise?

no

REVIEW

Decide whether each of the following statements is true or false:

1. Caffein is not a stimulant.

false

2. Any stimulant is an aid to relaxation.

false

3. Tea contains caffein.

true

4. No cola drinks contain caffein.

false

5. It is well for most people to restrict their intake of liquids after dinnertime.

true

6. A person who suffers from indigestion should eat something just before retiring.

false

7. Moderate daily physical exercise is an aid to sound sleep.

true

8. Heavy exercise should be performed just before going to bed.

false

9. Walking is an excellent form of moderate exercise.

true

10. Everyone should take a long walk just before going to bed.

false

THOUGHTS THAT PREVENT SLEEP

Comment on the following ways of
preparing for sleep:

Harold has a small but growing business
of his own; just before retiring for the
night he goes over the day's receipts
and makes plans for the next morning.
He finds that he continues thinking
about his problems long after he has
gone to bed.

If possible, business
problems should be
left at work. Try to
lock them outside the
door of your home.
If this is impossible,
learn to stop thinking
about them at least
an hour before you
go to bed.

Mildred says she hates television, but
she turns on her set as soon as she
arrives home from work. Throughout
the evening she switches channels
continually, watching program after
program with the hope that perhaps
she will finally find one that is less
boring than the others. She never
turns off the set before 1 a. m.
Mildred says that she watches
television because she cannot sleep.

If the truth were told,
Mildred probably
finds herself fighting
to stay awake.

After several hours of watching TV,
Mildred's eyes are strained and aching.
Even after she has turned off the TV
set and gone to bed, she still finds
herself trying to stare intensely through
closed lids. Instead of letting herself
sleep, she sometimes continues to think
of the hated TV programs for hours. In
our terms Mildred is doing everything
possible to - go to sleep/prevent sleep.

prevent sleep

During the past few years Betty has
followed the practice of going to bed
with a best-seller and "reading herself
to sleep." The fact that this doesn't
seem to work has not discouraged her.

Like Mildred,
Betty is
deliberately
providing herself
with exciting
stimuli at a
time when she
should be
thinking of sleep.

Betty's novel helps her to - sleep/stay awake.

stay awake

Both Betty and Mildred force themselves
to stay awake because they lack confidence
in their ability to sleep. Even after shutting
her book and turning out the light, Betty
often lies awake reliving parts of the story,
thinking of how it might have been changed,
and imagining various way to end it. Is
this a good way to invite sleep?

no

For unhappy people who are afraid to be
left alone, books and TV programs provide
not so much amusement as escape. In bed
such a person is no longer bombarded with
external stimuli; he lies awake with no
protection against unwelcome thoughts
about his life. A strong involvement in
neglected interests, a feeling of guilt for
having avoided personal problems, or a
compulsive need to resolve a number of
questions at once may extend this period
of wakefulness to an entire night.

Escapists must learn to

1.　face their problems during the
day.

2.　wrestle with problems throughout
the night.

1

Do escapists seem to be in need of some
way to "turn off their thoughts" when
trying to get to sleep?   yes

REVIEW

Decide whether each of the following
statements is true or false:

1. In the interests of relaxation,
   it's a good practice to bring
   home large amounts of office
   work.   false

2. If you do bring work home, you
   should stop thinking about it at
   least an hour before bedtime.   true

3. Watching television just before
   bedtime will help you to sleep.   false

4. Most people find it easy to "read
   themselves to sleep" with an
   exciting book.   false

5. Thinking about a story you've
   just read or a movie you've just
   seen will help you to sleep.   false

6. Unhappy people look at TV as
   much for escape as for
   amusement.   true

7. Escapists should try to resolve
   their problems after going to
   bed at night.   false

DRUGGING YOURSELF

We have just examined some ineffective
ways of preparing for sleep. Now let's
look at several very effective approaches
to the problem, which nonetheless have
certain drawbacks:

Martin has been troubled with insomnia
for many years. Lately he has found
that he goes right to sleep if he drinks
four ounces of whiskey just before retiring.

Martin is correct in thinking that alcohol
can act as a - stimulant/depressant.   depressant

As a sedative, alcohol has the following
disadvantages:

1. It - is/isn't - possible to build up   is
    a tolerance for alcohol, so that
    larger and larger amounts are
    required to give the same effect.

2. Alcohol is - often/never - habit   often
    forming.

3. Alcohol - frequently/never - has   frequently
    strong aftereffects.

Jessie uses sleeping tablets containing
barbiturates which are very effective in
putting her to sleep. She used to take
one tablet before going to sleep. She
now takes two.

Like alcohol, barbiturates - are/are not   are
depressants.

As sedatives, barbiturates are preferable
to alcohol. They are much cheaper and
more easily controlled. But like alcohol
they - can/cannot - be habit forming.   can

The side effects of barbiturates are usually
less severe than those from alcohol.
Barbiturates also carry with them less
danger of addiction; but they - are/are not -   are not
the most healthful way to induce sleep.

With the advent of effective tranquilizers,
barbiturates have been prescribed much
less frequently. Loretta always takes a
tranquilizer before going to bed. Is she
right in thinking that it helps her to sleep?   She probably is.

All tranquilizers are depressants; they
also have unpredictable and occasionally
serious side effects. They should not be
taken as a steady diet by normal people
because they mask rather than cure
problems, and they may be habit forming.

REVIEW

Decide whether each of the following
statements is true or false:

1. Alcohol can act as a depressant.   true

2. Several ounces of liquor taken
   just before going to bed will help
   to put most people to sleep.   true

3. Alcohol is the most effective and
   harmless sedative.   false

4. It is possible to build up a tolerance
   for alcohol.   true

5. Alcohol is habit forming in many
   cases.   true

6. Alcohol often has strong aftereffects.   true

7. As sedatives, barbiturates are
   usually preferable to alcohol.   true

8. Barbiturates can be habit forming.   true

9. There is danger of addiction to
   both alcohol and barbiturates.   true

10. No tranquilizers act as depressants.   false

11. Tranquilizers are the best way for
    the average person to cure his
    tensions.   false

12. Tranquilizers can be habit forming.   true

PREPARING FOR SLEEP

It is well to adopt a regular schedule in getting
ready for bed. This does not mean that you
have to cling compulsively to an exact sequence
of procedures, but a routine will help prevent   no (The basic
you from being exposed to tension-producing   idea is that of
stimuli just before or just after you go to bed.   gradually
Will you rush through this routine as fast as   relaxing into
possible?   sleep.)

Eventually this course will help you to remain
relaxed and happy in your work. At that time
you will no longer worry about "business
problems" even during the day. You will think
of your work as being at least as enjoyable as
the rest of your life.

For the moment, simply remember that any
problems at work constitute part of your
external environment, not your physical self.
Let your home be a place in which you enjoy
yourself and cater to your own personal needs.
If you need to placate your conscience at first,
console yourself with the thought that you will
be much more creative if you don't allow your
work to interfere with your sleep.

If you feel that you are forced to bring
work home, adopt the practice of attending
to it immediately after dinner. Should you
make it a rule to stop work at least one
hour before you plan to retire?   yes

Any work which you bring home should be
finished no later than 9:30 in the evening.
Then devote about an hour to some sort of
pleasant and undemanding activity. This
is the time for your hobby, for watching a
worthwhile TV show, or for reading.

In the interests of relaxation, would it be
even better if after dinner you could devote
yourself completely to leisure-time
activities?   yes

If you cannot do this, remember to spend a
minimum of - 15 minutes/one hour - in   one hour
activities which permit you to unwind before
you prepare for bed.

The next half hour should be spent in actually
getting ready for bed. You - should/shouldn't -   shouldn't
rush this process.

Always follow much the same routine in
undressing, hanging up your clothes,
brushing your teeth, etc. This procedure
will then become part of a habit pattern
which leads you directly and inevitably to
sleep. All of your movements should be

    1. swift and decisive.

    2. slow and leisurely.   2

If you find it hard to relax, spend the last 15
minutes of your final half-hour lying in a warm
bath. Close your eyes, breathe slowly and
deeply, and think of how good it will be to relax
in bed with no problems or worries.

When you emerge from your bath, don't
dry off by rubbing your body vigorously.
This would only wake you up. Pat yourself
dry with a towel; then go straight to bed.

During this time think only of how sleepy
you are. Don't dwell on today's problems
or worry about tomorrow.

Don't try to make plans. Tell yourself that
you are getting more and more relaxed and
comfortable; that you are very tired; that
you want to sleep.

Preparation for sleep should begin
- before/after - you go to bed.   before

How much time should you devote to   about half
getting ready for bed?   an hour

You will spend about 15 minutes of this
time brushing your teeth, undressing, etc.
During the remaining 15 minutes, many
tense people find it very relaxing to take
a...................   warm bath

While you are lying in the bath, your eyes
should be - open/closed.   closed

How do you breathe at this time?   slowly and
                                               deeply

Your thoughts should concern

   1.   your problems of the day.

   2.   your plans for tomorrow.

   3.   how good it is to relax without
        any worries.   3

REVIEW

Decide whether each of the following
statements are true or false:

1. If possible, it is best to leave
   your business problems at work.   true

2. You should establish a regular
   routine in preparing for bed.   true

3. You should prepare for bed as
   fast as possible.   false

4. A cold shower is just as relaxing
   as a warm bath.   false
   (If it doesn't
   give you a heart
   attack, it will
   at least wake
   you up.)

5. A warm shower is as relaxing as
   a warm bath.   false
   (You can relax
   much more
   successfully
   while you lie
   in the bath.)

6. After you finish your bath, you should
   rub yourself vigorously with a towel.   false
   (You should pat
   yourself gently.)

From your bath you should go

1. to watch TV

2. straight to bed.

3. to read a good novel.

4. to the refrigerator   2

Once in bed, you should think only of

1. going to sleep.

2. what a fool you made of yourself
   during the day.

3. your business plans.

4. your budget.   1

A PLACE DEVOTED TO SLEEP

Remember to leave all problems locked
outside your bedroom door. The bedroom
should be a place which is wholly devoted
to sleep.

There is only one small exception to this
rule. Some people find that their most
imaginative ideas occur to them when they
are fully relaxed. They know that they
should think only of going to sleep, but
they worry about forgetting their inspirations,
and by worrying they keep themselves awake.

If you find this happening to you, place a
pencil and a pad of paper near your bed.
Then if any new idea or problem occurs
to you, jot the details down on the pad so
that you can look at them in the morning
when you are refreshed. This permits
you to relax and sleep, assured that your
ideas won't be lost.

What should you think about while you
lie in bed?

going to sleep

What should you do if a good idea occurs
to you?

Write it down,
and then put it
out of your
mind.

Keep your bedroom as dark and as quiet
as possible. Don't litter it with reminders
of your working day. If you need to work
at a desk, should it be placed in the bedroom?

Not if it will
fit anywhere
else.

Should you have a TV set in your bedroom?

Not unless you
are an invalid.

Don't feel that you have to be a fresh air fiend who sleeps with all the windows wide open. Opening one window a crack will provide you with plenty of fresh air, while preventing the entrance of undue noise or icy blasts of wind.

Instead of several heavier blankets, you may prefer to use an electric blanket. With a control to adjust temperature at your fingertips, you don't have to keep extra blankets at the bottom of the bed, where they weigh uncomfortably on your feet; and you won't lie awake and shiver for hours while you try to decide whether or not you really want to get up and look for more blankets.

Let's suppose that you are using an electric blanket. You wake up in the middle of the night because you are too warm or too cold.

(1) Do you have to decide how many blankets to throw on or off?

no

(2) Do you have to tense your muscles with the exercise of looking for blankets or throwing them off?

no

(3) Do you have to get up to open or close a window, or to adjust the thermostat that changes the temperature of the room?

no
(An adjustment of your blanket's thermostat will compensate for all but the most extreme changes in temperature.)

REVIEW

Decide whether each of the following
statements is true or false:

1. No one should keep a pad and
   pencil at his bedside.   false

2. You should keep your bedroom as
   dark and as quiet as possible.   true

3. In order to sleep soundly, you must
   have at least one bedroom window
   open.   false

4. Watching TV is an excellent way to
   put yourself to sleep.   false

5. You should never use an electric
   blanket.   false

6. If you can afford it, it's a good idea
   to soundproof your bedroom.   true

7. Your window drapes, blinds, etc.,
   should be arranged to prevent light
   and noise from entering.   true

8. Very heavy blankets are an aid to
   slumber.   false

9. An electric blanket helps you to
   avoid uncomfortable pressure
   while you relax in preparation
   for sleep.   true

10. It also allows you to make adjustments
    in temperature without tensing your
    muscles to throw off excess blankets,
    or getting up to find extra ones.   true

TRYING NOT TO SLEEP

As we have seen, sound sleep is a habit.
Is insomnia also a habit?   yes

An established routine or pattern can lead
you to sleep. Similarly, whatever interrupts
sleep one night is more likely to interrupt
it the next; thus a pattern of _____   insomnia
can easily be established.

Does a person with a strongly established
pattern of insomnia have confidence in his
ability to sleep?   no

Such a person always insists that he is
trying his best to sleep, but an observer
would find that the insomniac is doing
everything possible to - induce/prevent -   prevent
sleep.

Insomniacs make desperate efforts to get
to sleep. They fume and fret, tumble and
toss, shift and move, hang halfway out of
the bed, wrap themselves in the bedclothes,
double up, lash about with their legs,
pummel their pillows, and in general conduct
themselves as if they hated the mattress and
were engaged in a wrestling match with it.
They say that they are doing all this because
they can't sleep.

A behaviorist might find it more meaningful
to say that insomniacs can't sleep because of
all this activity. Sleep is not to be wooed so
energetically. As we have seen, muscles
which are being used are necessarily
- tense/relaxed.   tense

Whenever you move your body, some groups
of muscles must be performing work. Every
time you roll over in bed, many muscles
participate in the effort. Does this repeated
tensing of your muscles keep you awake?   yes

Is it possible for muscle groups to remain
perfectly relaxed when they are being used
to change the position of your body?   no

Therefore, when practicing relaxation, you
should always

  1. hold yourself as stiff as a board.

  2. lie quietly.

  3. shift constantly in search of a
      comfortable position.   2

Decide whether each of the following
statements is true or false:

  1. If you can't sleep, you should spend
      your time twisting and turning in
      search of a comfortable position.   false

  2. Great physical exertion is required
      for sleep.   false

  3. Worrying about your inability to
      sleep will help you to doze off.   false

  4. Muscles which are being used to
      move your body are necessarily
      tense.   true

  5. Absolute rigidity is a symptom of
      tension.   true

You may well object that you can't lie still
when you are uncomfortable, and that all
this shifting about and tossing in bed is
simply an effort to find a comfortable
position.   But you must remember that
no position can remain comfortable for
long unless you achieve general relaxation.
Remember also that movements necessarily
involve tension in your muscles.   Is this
tension an enemy of sleep?   yes

Suppose that you hold yourself so rigid
that you literally do not move a muscle.
Will this also involve tension which will
prevent you from sleeping?   yes

When you lie down to sleep, you should
neither move nor hold yourself rigid.
Either alternative involves _____   tension
in your muscles.

How are you to remain motionless without
becoming tense? In this course the answer
is almost a matter of definition.   You will
_____ all your muscles.   relax

Tense muscles ache and demand movement.
This constant tossing about will - encourage/
prevent - sleep.   prevent

Only by relaxing can you lie motionless and
still remain comfortable. But this requires
more advanced techniques of relaxation than
those which we have practiced thus far.

PREPARING TO RELAX

We will now discuss the powerful technique
of progressive relaxation, which puts you
to sleep by eliminating the final tensions
from your body.

You will be able to perform some of the
following exercises as you read, but for
the most of them you will have to close the
book and turn out the lights.

After you have read the next few pages and
made the appropriate responses, you will be
prepared to practice progressive relaxation
with your eyes closed when you decide to sleep.
You will have learned both the technique of
progressive relaxation and the reasons for
using it.

Imagine that you have just gone to bed. First
you will employ the six aids to general relaxation
which you have already learned. These are . . . . .

smiling
yawning
stretching
closing your
eyes
deep breathing
repetition of
the word "relax"

Close your eyes, stretch and yawn, breathe
deeply, repeat the word "relax" several times,
and start the process of progressive relaxation
with a smile on your face.

As you use your six aids to general relaxation,
you will feel some of the tension disappearing
from your muscles, but considerable hidden
tension will remain. It is this _____
tension which we will now eliminate by a
process of step-by-step specific relaxation.

hidden

Prepare yourself for the process of progressive
_____ by lying on your back, with   relaxation
your arms extended down and outward from your
sides.

Let's review this position so that you can
literally practice it with your eyes closed.
You are lying on your - stomach/side/back.   back

Your arms are

1. folded behind your head.

2. lying well out from your sides.

3. folded across your chest.

4. tight against your sides.   2

As you read the following chapters, don't
worry about the actual location of the
voluntary muscles in your body. We are
concerned only with the points at which
you feel their relaxation.

PROGRESSIVE RELAXATION

Begin by consciously relaxing your feet. At
this point you should feel your heels resting
heavily against the bed. Should you be trying
to hold your heels up from the bed?   no

Your _____ are now resting heavily against   ˙heels
the bed. Next relax the muscles of your lower
legs.

After your feet are thoroughly relaxed and your
heels are resting heavily against the bed, you
relax the muscles of your - upper/lower - legs.   lower

You now have two points where there is a feeling
of weight resting heavily against the bed--your
_____ and the backs of your lower _____.   heels, legs

Relax your upper legs. They should seem
to move - toward/away from - the bed.   toward

Check to be sure that all the muscles in
your legs and feet are now _____,   relaxed
and that no muscle groups are trying to
hold your legs up off the bed.

All through your legs you should now have
the feeling of letting go completely. Should
both legs feel limp and heavy as if you had
just dropped them onto the bed?   yes

Relax your lower back. In what direction
does it seem to move?   toward the bed

After relaxing the muscles of your _____   lower
back, relax the muscles of your upper back.

Now that you have relaxed the muscles of
your lower and upper _____, relax your   back
shoulders, and make sure that they too are
resting heavily against the bed.

You relaxed first the muscles of your feet,
then your lower legs, upper _____, lower   legs
back, and upper _____.   back

Then you relaxed your shoulders and made
sure that they were resting - lightly/heavily -   heavily
against the bed.

You should now feel weight against the bed at
the following points: your shoulders, upper
back, lower back, upper legs, lower legs,
and _____.   heels

Check these spots mentally, starting with your
heels. Make sure that you - are/are not -   are not
trying to hold your weight away from the bed
at the contact points.

Now focus your attention on the muscles of
your upper arms, feeling them relax and
settle limply on the bed.

As you relax the muscles of your upper _____,   arms
you will feel your elbows resting heavily
against the bed.

Moving downward from your elbows, relax
the muscles of your forearms and hands.
Does this make you feel even more weight
on your elbows?   yes

You have now relaxed the muscles of your
upper arms, forearms and _____.   hands

Your arms are now completely relaxed. Step
by step, you have eliminated tensions from
each _____ group as you moved from your   muscle
shoulders down to your hands.

Relax the muscles at the back of your neck.
As you do this, you should feel your head
settle heavily against the pillow. Was this
the last major part of your body which tensed
muscles were still straining to hold away
from the bed?   yes

Now move your attention downward across the
front of your body, relaxing the muscles of your
throat, your chest and your stomach. Again
check the muscle groups which you have already
relaxed. Are your head, shoulders, thighs,
calves and heels resting heavily against the bed?   They should be.

Now start with your heels once more and
move upward, checking your calves, thighs,
lower back, upper back, shoulders and head
to make sure that all of these points are   heavily against
completely relaxed and resting . . . .   the bed.
                                       (how)

No groups of muscles should now be tightened
in an effort to hold parts of your body up from
the bed. The muscles in your throat, chest
and _____, which are not in contact   stomach
with the bed, should also be relaxed.

Check to make sure that your arms are
completely relaxed, with your _____   elbows
and hands resting heavily against the bed.

THE MOST IMPORTANT MUSCLES AGAIN

Are the muscles of the face region crucial in
achieving a state of relaxation?   yes

First relax the muscles of your scalp; then
relax your forehead, your cheeks, and the
tiny muscles around your mouth.

When you relax your cheeks, let your jaw
sag downward. Let your tongue "float"
limply in your mouth. You should get the
same feeling of - tension/release - that   release
you had when you relaxed your clenched
fist in our first set of exercises.

As you doubtless remember, in terms of
relaxation the most important muscles in
the entire body are those of your _____.   eyes

The sensation of _____ in your eyes
is the same feeling of "letting go" which you
had when you relaxed your biceps muscles.

relaxation

Your eyes should feel as if they are loose in
their sockets and about to drop out. When
you have this feeling of release in your eyes,
you can be sure that they are completely

_____.

relaxed

You relax your _____ muscles to the point
where you can no longer actively visualize
images.

eye

When your _____ are so relaxed that they
feel ready to drop out of their sockets, be
sure that you have not allowed tension to
creep back into the muscles of your mouth.

eyes

Your jaw should be sagging and the muscles
of speech should be completely relaxed.
When these muscles are relaxed to a point
where you can no longer form words, you
have nearly ceased to think.

We might describe thinking in terms of the
processes of visualizing images and of
forming _____ with the muscles of speech.

words

If you really succeed in relaxing your eyes
and muscles of speech to the point where
you can no longer visualize images or form
_____, you will be asleep.

words

The most important points for you to check
and relax several times are the muscles of
your eyes and the muscles of _____.

speech

FURTHER COMMENTS

If you had followed these instructions faithfully
while actually lying in bed, you would probably
be asleep. If not, you would now be experiencing
the delightful sensation of release that comes
from complete _____.   relaxation

You have just learned a technique of step-by-
step relaxation which gives you full control
over the voluntary muscle groups in your body.
Do you find that it allows you to relax more
thoroughly than you could have simply by saying   All readers
"relax all over"?   answered yes.

Somewhat later you will develop the ability to
achieve similar results by saying "relax."
But this will come only after long practice.

Now repeat the process of step-by-step
relaxation which we have just described.
Starting with your feet, specifically relax
each muscle group until you reach your
scalp muscles. Then start with your facial
muscles and specifically relax the muscle
groups in the front of your body until you
reach your feet again. If you find that you've
forgotten some of the steps, check with the
program.

We have discussed step-by-step specific
relaxation as if each part of your body were
independent of the others.

In actual practice, as a result of the feedback
mechanism which we mentioned previously,
the complete relaxation of any part of your
body causes all the other parts to become
- more/less - relaxed.   more

As a consequence, many people fall asleep
long before they have consciously relaxed
all parts of the body. Relaxation of some
muscle groups causes the others to relax
sufficiently to induce sleep.

ADDITIONAL TECHNIQUES

If you complete the process of progressive
relaxation and find yourself still awake,
repeat the word <u>fluid</u>. Associate this word
with a sensation of release in all the tiny
_____ groups throughout your body.   muscle

As you repeat the word _____, your   fluid
entire body should feel liquid and limp, as
if you were floating on a sea of sleep.

If you still find yourself awake, repeat the
word <u>heavy</u> several times.

When you have succeeded in properly relaxing
the muscles of speech, you will find that it is
hard to remember what you are supposed to do.
You will pronounce the words <u>fluid</u> and <u>heavy</u>

    1.   rapidly and easily.

    2.   slowly and indistinctly.   2

As you pronounce the word _____, you   heavy
should feel a sensation of enormous weight
in your arms and legs.

Tell yourself that your arms and _____   legs
are as heavy as lead.

Your _____ and legs should feel as if they   arms
are falling off your body because of their
enormous weight.

If you are not asleep before you have
finished the process of progressive
relaxation, you will find it helpful to
repeat the words _____ and _____.   fluid,   heavy

Here is another very useful device:
Consciously imitate the breathing pattern
of a person who is falling asleep.   Take
regular, slow, deep breaths.

Have you already used a similar technique
as an aid to general relaxation?   yes

Tension causes you to use lots of oxygen.
When you are relaxed, you need much less.
As a consequence your breathing slows, and
the rest period between breathing out and
breathing in becomes - shorter/longer.   longer

You will immediately realize that this type
of slow, rhythmic breathing has always
preceded your going to sleep, and that it
is similar to the breathing of the sleeping
people you have observed.

As you exhale, say to yourself "let go and
relax. "   Will the muscles of the rest of
your body tend to relax along with your chest
muscles?   yes

Consciously lengthen the pause between
breathing out and breathing in. You will
feel a sense of utter relaxation and well being
which is the - same as/exact opposite of -   exact opposite of
the breathless gasping and panting of nervous
people.

REVIEW

Decide whether each of the following
statements is true or false:

1. As you lie down and prepare for
   progressive relaxation, you should
   hold your body absolutely rigid.   false

2. If you feel very uncomfortable and
   you have to move constantly, you
   are not sufficiently relaxed.   true

3. When you are sufficiently relaxed,
   you won't feel the muscle tensions
   which cause you to want to move.   true

4. Step-by-step relaxation is also
   called progressive relaxation.   true

5. You prepare for progressive relaxation
   by lying on your stomach.   false

6. Your arms are held tight against your sides.   false

7. You should use the six aids to general
   relaxation before beginning step-by-step
   relaxation.   true

8. You begin progressive relaxation by
   consciously relaxing your feet.   true

9. When your legs are relaxed, they
   should feel limp and heavy.   true

10. In terms of progressive relaxation, the
    most important muscles are those of your neck.   false

11. If you relax your eyes and muscles of
    speech to the point where you can no
    longer actively visualize images or form
    words, you will fall asleep.   true

12. The relaxation of any part of your body causes
    all other parts to become more relaxed.   true

13. Rapid, shallow breathing will help you to
    go to sleep.   false

14. Tense, excited people breathe slowly.   false

15. You should try to shorten the period
    between breathing out and breathing in.   false

16. Imitating the rhythmical breathing of a
    sleeping person helps to induce sleep.   true

FOUR STEPS IN GOING TO SLEEP

If you wish to think of the techniques which
we have just discussed as four steps in going
to sleep, you might consider that Step 1 is
the process of progressive _____.   relaxation

Step 2 consists of thinking the word _____,   fluid
while you feel all the tiny muscle groups let
go, until your whole body feels limp and almost
liquid.

In Step 3 you repeat the word _____ and   heavy
feel a sensation of heaviness in your arms
and legs.

Step 4 includes slow, deep, rhythmic_____   breathing
and the repetition of the words "let go and
relax" as you exhale.

Obviously there is nothing magic about such
words as heavy, fluid, or let go and relax.
But most people who have taken this program
have found that habits of relaxation become
strongly associated with these words.

You may find that the four steps outlined
above suffice to put you to sleep. The next
part of this program is for those who have
had severe sleeping problems for a number
of years. If you don't belong to this
distinguished group, skip to the section
entitled RESPONDING TO KEY WORDS
on page 147.

FOR CONFIRMED INSOMNIACS ONLY

Some people have deeply established habits
which compete with the techniques of
relaxation. Strongly ingrained patterns of
insomnia are hard to eliminate.

Insomniacs have one mistake in common.
Instead of banishing their cares, they
insist on thinking about problems, projects,
or past experiences; they hang on to these
thoughts desperately in the face of approaching
sleep.

Many habitually tense people can't imagine
vacating their minds of thought and giving
their bodies over totally to the sensation of
relaxation. They fear the onset of sleep as
some sort of attack on their personalities
or encroachment on their lives, and they
fight in every way to prevent its occurrence.
If questioned, such people complain of
insomnia, and say that they have done everything possible to induce sleep.

Are deeply established patterns of insomina
easy to eliminate?   no

Do confirmed insomniacs find it hard to
imagine a state of complete relaxation?   yes

If you are an insomniac, it may take you
some time to overcome the habit of
concentration on fixed ideas which you
refuse to relinquish at bedtime. You can
make a start by reminding yourself that
when you go to bed you are in a situation
where no demands are being made on you,
and where no one can threaten you or hurt
you. Remember that any conscious effort
to continue concentrating on your waking
thoughts - will/won't - prevent you from   will
sleeping.

You will be able to deal with your problems
much more effectively

1.   at night when you are tired.

2.   in the morning when you are rested.   2

Many insomniacs seem to feel that it is their
duty to stay awake. If this is your problem,
remind yourself that you - have/don't have -   have
the right to sleep.

Is there any outside force which demands that
you sacrifice your sleep to self-torture?   Of course not.

Should you devote your nights to grappling   Not if you want
restlessly with personal problems?   to sleep.

Must you go to bed only to relive humiliating   Congress has
or frustrating experiences?   passed no such
          law.

Will dwelling with dread on possible future
catastrophies make you more effective in
dealing with them or make tomorrow more
secure?   no

In addition to prolonging your period of
wakefulness, the behavior mentioned above
- increases/diminishes - your anxieties   increases
and frustrations.

The more you practice thwarting your body's
need for sleep, the more successful an insomniac
you become. Is there anyone anywhere who
demands that you writhe in emotional anguish   No one but
while tucked snugly in your own bed?   yourself.

Should you feel guilty for refusing to think of
unpleasant things while you prepare yourself
for sleep?   no

The interval before sleep has such painful
associations for a true insomniac that he
uses every excuse to avoid going to bed.
When he finally does find himself in bed,
he refuses to relinquish his tight hold on
his thoughts.

Even when you try to banish competing
thoughts, they may still occur. If they
do, simply repeat slowly to yourself
I am going to sleep.

Never ask yourself, "Am I really going to
sleep?" or "Am I asleep yet?" Such
questions awaken the conscious part of you
that examines things. They cause a state
of tension and worry which tends to prevent
you from sleeping. You cannot force yourself
to sleep.

REVIEW

Relaxation is the absence of _____.   tension

Tension always accompanies effort.   Any
conscious effort

1.   prevents you from sleeping.

2.   helps you to sleep.

3.   has nothing to do with sleep.   1

Plenty of sleep should be viewed as

1.   a waste of time.

2.   an admission of physical weakness.

3.   a requirement of your body, which
     will make your waking hours more
     productive and enjoyable.   3

Should you try to hurry yourself to sleep?   no

Conscious _____ is an enemy of sleep.   effort

What are some of the questions you should   Am I really
never ask yourself?   going to sleep?

Am I asleep yet?

Without making any conscious effort to   I am going to
force yourself to sleep, you should simply   sleep.
repeat . . . .

Decide whether each of the following
statements is true or false:

1. When you wish to go to sleep, you
   should try to vacate your mind of
   conscious thought.   true

2. As you relax in preparation for sleep,
   it is good to remind yourself that you
   are in a situation where no one can
   threaten you or hurt you.   true

3. This will help to prevent you from
   viewing the onset of sleep as an
   attack on your personality.   true

4. You should stop occasionally and
   check your progress in relaxation
   by asking "Am I asleep yet?"   false

5. You should form the habit of letting
   your mind dwell on the same problems
   every night in order to induce sleep.   false

6. You owe it to yourself and other to
   lie awake wrestling with your problems
   far into the night.   false

A LAST RESORT FOR DESPERATE CASES

Read this only if you are so preoccupied with
your problems that you mind still tries to think
about them in spite of all the techniques of
relaxation you have learned.

The next exercise will provide you with a
mental activity which will at first compete
with your disturbing preoccupations, then
finally relegate them to obscurity. You will
start by counting backward from 200, while
repeating "I am going to _____."   sleep

After you have become really proficient at
using the techniques of relaxation, you will
no longer need this device to discipline your
mind. But it may take some months for a
confirmed insomniac to reach this point.
Until you do, you can prevent the intrusion
of unwelcome thoughts by _____ slowly   counting
backward from 200.

Between each number you will repeat ·········   I am going to
                                                sleep.

Thus you will say:

    200   I am going to sleep.

    ___   I am going to sleep.   199

    198   _____   I am going to
                                                sleep.

    ___   _____   197, I am going
                                                to sleep.

Again, there is nothing magic about the number
200 or the process of counting backward. But
the feat has been found just difficult enough to
prevent a tired person from concentrating on
his personal problems. When going to sleep,
it is better to banish all conscious thought
than to count, but it is better to count than to
worry about your boss's opinion of you.

If you have suffered from insomnia for some
years, and have formed the habit of taking
sleeping tablets, use the techniques of
relaxation to help you reduce the dosage
gradually. When you become proficient in
relaxation, you - will/will not - need to rely   will not
on sedatives in order to sleep.

Remember to avoid thinking "I have to go to
sleep." This thought will cause conscious
effort which will prevent you from sleeping.

Many insomniacs indulge in monologues
such as the following: "It's 1:30 and I'm
still awake... I have to get up at 7:30...
that makes only six hours of sleep even if
I go to sleep right now... come on, come
on, go to sleep..."

Eventually the insomniac turns on the light to
check the time. It's 2:30, and the reflection
that he will now get only five hours of sleep,
even if he goes to sleep at once, starts him off
on another monologue. At 3:30 he is worrying
about when he will ever have time to take a nap
to make up for a sleepless night. By 4:30 he is
sitting up in bed staring at the clock, etc.

After a sleepless night, the insomniac remains
dull and sluggish throughout the day. He hasn't
sufficient energy to take any exercise. When
bedtime comes, his body feels no need for sleep.
Thus the pattern of the previous night repeats
itself.

Don't imitate our typical insomniac's mistakes.
Once you have banished the tensions of the day
and gone through all the steps of progressive
relaxation, you should find it very pleasant to
lie in bed. Relaxation should seem so enjoyable
that you feel in no real hurry to sleep.

If your comfort is disturbed by thoughts of
facing the next day after a bout with insomnia,
remind yourself that there is no law that says
you have to go to sleep. Are you already
resting when you are completely relaxed?   yes

As your initial objective, decide that you will
remain in bed in a relaxed state for at least
eight hours a night. Don't worry about whether
or not you sleep during this time. Consider that
you have succeeded if you lie comfortably in bed
without having to get up and turn the light on,
read, watch television, get something to eat or
drink, etc.

A state of complete general relaxation is
- more/less - beneficial than troubled sleep.   more

Will any insistence on going to sleep defeat
your purpose?   yes

Learn to enjoy the state of relaxation and to
make no conscious effort to sleep. Soon you
will find that you have cut your period of
wakefulness in half.

SUMMARY

When you are preparing to retire, remember
to think only about relaxing and sleeping.

If you are preoccupied with other things while
preparing for bed, you may still be very
excited when you lie down to sleep.

When you find that you are breathing rapidly
and your heart is beating fast, or that you
have some of the other signs of tension,
repeat Step 1, the process of progressive
_____, as many times as you find   relaxation
necessary to relax yourself completely.

If you cannot sleep, should you worry about the
effects that a sleepless night will have on your
activities the next day?   no

If you remain perfectly relaxed, will you
benefit from the rest you obtain during the
time spent going to sleep?   yes

After a few months of faithful practice, even
people who previously relied on sleeping pills
have learned to go to sleep in less than five
minutes.

RESPONDING TO KEY WORDS

For the first few weeks you will go through
your full routine of progressive relaxation,
or as much of it as is necessary to put you
to sleep.

As you follow the same steps night after night,
the entire process will become automatic. You
will not have to repeat the lengthy technique of
specific relaxation of the muscle groups in
various parts of your body. The word _____   relax
will be sufficient to relax you completely.

We then say that you have conditioned yourself
to the key word _____.   relax

If you have formed the habit of using the other
steps, you will find that they too become
automatic. You will need only the key word
_____ to feel your entire body become   fluid
limp and almost liquid, as all the tiny muscle
groups let go.

The key word _____ will immediately make   heavy
your arms and legs feel as heavy as lead.

The key word _____ will automatically   breathe
lead to the slow, deep, rhythmic breathing of
sleep.

All these words will be useful to you in putting
yourself to sleep, but the first and most important
key word, _____, can also be used in the   relax
morning when you wake up, and frequently during
the day.

Once you have mastered progressive relaxation,
the word _____ suffices to eliminate tension   relax
from all the muscles of your body.

When you first wake up in the morning after a
good night's sleep, you are naturally relaxed.
It's the best time to remind yourself to stay
that way throughout the entire day.

The first words you should say when you wake up
in the morning are, "I'm going to remain _____   relaxed
throughout the entire day."

If you are very tense and worried during the day,
you will find it much harder to stop thinking about
your problems at night. But if you learn to remain
relaxed throughout the day, you will have taken a
big step in the direction not only of sound sleep but
also of personal happiness.

If you find yourself becoming tense at any time
during the day, simply repeat the word _____.   relax

If the word <u>relax</u> itself doesn't give immediate
results, it means that you are not yet thoroughly
conditioned to it. Take a few minutes to go
through the entire process of step-by-step
relaxation. It can never do you any harm.

In situations where you find yourself becoming
almost hysterical, you may even wish to use
all the key words. They can help you out of
many a nervous crisis.

Give the four key words which, with proper   relax, fluid,
conditioning, will help you to achieve a state   heavy, breathe
of relaxation.

At first you may find it hard to remember to
relax in situations which have previously been
very difficult for you. Don't be discouraged by
initial failures. The very fact that you find
yourself in a state of tension should be a
reminder to use your techinques of _____.   relaxation

Once you have learned to identify symptoms
of tension in your body, and to admit to
yourself that excessive tension is making
your life less pleasant than it might otherwise
be, you have taken an enormous step forward.
Most people attribute the tensions which they
carry with them to their external environment.
If you accept the fact that it is - yourself/your
environment - that is in need of adjustment, you   yourself
are well on the road to self-control.

When you find yourself growing tense, congratulate
yourself on having learned to identify tension, and
on knowing how to go about eliminating it. Don't
brand yourself a fool and a failure. This sort of
masochism will only make you even more tense.

As we mentioned before, it will help to write the word _____ on slips of paper, to be left in such likely places as your wallet, top desk drawer, the glove compartment in your car, etc.

relax

Be constantly on your guard against the onset of tension. To refresh your memory, decide whether each of the items in the following list is a symptom of tension or of relaxation:

1.	drinking coffee constantly	tension
2.	slow, graceful movements	relaxation
3.	trembling	tension
4.	eating slowly	relaxation
5.	drumming with your fingers	tension
6.	indigestion	tension
7.	a rigid, cramped position	tension
8.	ability to wait patiently	relaxation
9.	biting nails	tension
10.	slow, deep breathing	relaxation
11.	stumbling speech	tension
12.	criticizing others	tension
13.	fidgeting	tension
14.	stretching	relaxation
15.	cracking knuckles	tension
16.	ability to process new information in a group situation	relaxation
17.	feeling of guilt	tension
18.	beating time with your feet	tension
19.	inability to describe what you've seen in the movies or on TV	tension

20.	twisting and grimacing	tension
21.	calmness	relaxation
22.	fear of wasting time	tension
23.	a high-pitched, metallic voice	tension
24.	ability to express a controversial opinion in public	relaxation
25.	spasmodic coughing	tension
26.	excessive perspiration	tension
27.	cramped, painful handwriting	tension
28.	inability to concentrate	tension
29.	blushing	tension
30.	smiling	relaxation
31.	frequent trips to the bathroom	tension
32.	irritability	tension
33.	frequent headaches	tension
34.	scowling	tension
35.	sensitivity to noise or to other people's mannerisms	tension
36.	constant fiddling with small objects	tension
37.	overactivity	tension
38.	frequent stomach aches	tension
39.	biting lips	tension
40.	self-confidence	relaxation
41.	very frequent, compulsive eating	tension
42.	insomnia	tension
43.	very rapid speech	tension
44.	chain smoking	tension
45.	yawning	relaxation
46.	frequent skin rashes	tension
47.	a low, pleasant voice	relaxation

TENSIONS CAUSED BY PEOPLE

In our society, most tension-producing situations
are associated with other people. At first you
will probably find it much easier to remain
relaxed when you are - with people/alone.

alone

When you are with other people, there is a
tendency for you to worry about their opinion
of you, and to act in a way which you think they
will find correct or admirable. The rare
people who don't worry much about others'
opinions tend to be very - tense/relaxed.

relaxed

Conversely, people who are very relaxed don't
tend to worry much about the opinions of others.
In your experience, are such people generally
happier than those who worry constantly about
what sort of impression they are making?

Most readers
answered yes.

Your final triumph will come when people are no
longer able to upset you. You will then remain
relaxed and comfortable with yourself throughout
the rest of your life. But it takes considerable
practice for most of us to reach this stage. At
first you may have to be satisfied with learning
how to relax and remain relaxed when you are
- with others/alone.

alone

As you become more and more relaxed, you will
be less concerned with other people's opinions,
and better able to examine your own behavior.
Even in situations with other people, you will
monitor your own reactions. Whenever you
find that you are becoming tense, you will be
able to remind yourself to _____.

relax

For the time being, observations of other people
will give you the best training for recognizing
tension in interpersonal relationships. Let's
examine a series of situations in which the
principal characters involved show definite signs
of tension. You will have an opportunity to
diagnose their problems and to suggest possible
solutions.

THE MINK STOLE

It is a lovely spring day. In a hurry to drop
the children off at school, Elsie Smith pulls
an old trench coat on over her slacks and
sweater.

Driving back from the school, Elsie notices a
sensational fur sale at the most exclusive shop
in town. She has wanted a mink stole for years;
this looks like an opportunity to pick one up at a
bargain price and store it for the following winter.

The thought of the way she is dressed makes
Elsie smile and shake her head, but she parks
her car and enters the store, looking for her
favorite sales girl.

The sales girl is nowhere to be found. It seems
to be her day off. None of the other girls pay
any attention to Elsie.

At the jewelry counter Elsie asks where she may
see the furs that are on sale. The girl behind the
counter looks Elsie slowly up and down, and then
says icily, "Perhaps you'd best try the fur department." She then presents Elsie with her profile,
and returns to her self-appointed task of staring
out the window.

At this point an appropriate reaction from Mrs.
Smith might be

1. to give the girl a good piece of her mind.

2. to say that she understands this, but that
   she is interested in the location of the
   counter at which the fur sale is taking
   place.

3. to walk out of the store.

4. to ask to speak to the manager.

2
(Any other
response shows
anger and tension,
and attributes too
much importance
to the salesgirl's
opinion.)

Elsie does none of these things. She turns
furiously to another counter, where two
sales girls are discussing a movie. She
stands at the counter for several minutes.
Without paying the slightest attention to her,
the sales girls continue their conversation,
while Elsie's impatience and anger mount.

In terms of achieving her goal of buying the
mink stole, Mrs. Smith's most appropriate
reaction at this point is to

1. Tell the sales girls that they are
   very impolite.

2. wait at the counter until they notice
   her, even if it takes hours.

3. say, "Excuse me for interrupting,
   but could you direct me to the
   counter where the furs are on sale?"

3
(The other
alternatives
presuppose a
responsibility on
Elsie's part to
teach the sales
girls manners,
or to await their
pleasure. Either
solution attributes
more importance
to the girls'
opinions than to
Elsie's own
peace of mind.)

But Elsie says nothing at all. Almost in tears,
she finds the fur sale for herself. Braving the
contemptuous stare of the girl behind the counter,
she asks if she may see the mink stoles. Without
a word, the girl shows her one.

Elsie asks to see something a little less expensive.
Smugly the girl tells her that she will have to
understand that by its very nature mink just isn't
cheap. Elsie answers that she is very grateful for
this bit of invaluable information, and asks the girl
if she learned it all by herself.

Elsie then makes a final attempt to retain her own
ego picture and justify herself in the eyes of the
sales girl. Fumbling in her pocketbook, she pulls
out a charge card, which she thrusts under the
girl's nose. In a shrill and uncontrolled voice she
tells the girl that she has had an account with the
store for five years, and has never before met with
such insolence. She then hurries away.

Almost blinded by tears of rage, and in a
state of tension verging on hysteria, Elsie
has to sit in her car for ten minutes before
she is sufficiently calm to drive away.

If Elsie Smith had been relaxed enough to keep
her objective in mind, a more appropriate
reaction to the salesgirl's comment on the
cost of mink might have been

1. to say that she knows more about
   mink than any sales girl.

2. to try to explain to the girl the way
   in which mink is priced.

3. to say that she didn't ask for a lot
   of stupid advice; she just wants to
   see a cheaper mink stole.

4. to smile and say that she is sure the
   girl is right, but that she is still
   interested in something a bit less
   expensive.   4

At this point could Elsie still have mastered
the situation simply by extracting her credit
card, and saying that she would like to select
something from a lower price range and charge
it to her regular account?   yes

The way in which Mrs. Smith did use her
credit card

1. helped her to accomplish her goal
   of buying the fur piece.

2. showed the salesgirl that Elsie was
   in complete command of the situation.

3. intensified an unpleasant situation to
   a point where Elsie will probably
   hesitate to return to the fur sale, no
   matter how well she is dressed.   3

Mrs. Smith found herself in a situation which
can easily produce a state of tension in most
women. They find it hard to face the self-
assured insolence of a salesgirl who achieves
her only satisfaction by identifying with the
luxurious appointments in a store, and who
judges her customers solely by their clothes.

Many readers will feel sorry for Elsie Smith.
She herself was sure that it was the attitude
of the salesgirls which made her unhappy. But
if she is to prevent the repetition of such
occurrences, she will have to

1. avoid entering exclusive shops.

2. attribute less importance to the
   opinions of salesgirls.

3. see that she is always perfectly
   dressed.

4. abandon all hope of wearing mink.

5. practice sharp retorts.   2

If Elsie were capable of remaining somewhat
more relaxed, her reactions would not be
those of a person who feels that she must
constantly defend a self-image.

A more relaxed Elsie would realize that salesgirls do not lead easy lives: they are under
constant supervision; they are required to look
their best at all times and to be on their feet
the entire day; they are paid low salaries and
are often ignored by customers or treated
disdainfully. The expensive clothes which they
buy at special prices from the store at which
they work are sometimes their only badge of
superiority.

Like too many of us, sales girls are often
tense people who feel the need to assert their
importance. Since they are so often looked
down upon, they seek opportunities to look
down on others.

In the incident which we just described, the
salesgirls tried to demonstrate their superiority
to Elsie Smith. Did they triumph over her
by getting just the reactions they desired?

yes

Would you guess that the particular salesgirls
that Elsie encountered were happy, relaxed
people?

probably not

If Elsie had realized this fact, she might have
approached the girls differently. Might she
then have received somewhat different reactions
from them?

yes

If Elsie had known of progressive relaxation,
should she have practiced it when she reached
her car?

yes

She should also have reminded herself of the
fact that happiness lies

1.   in the number of mink stoles you
      possess.

2.   in the opinions of others.

3.   within yourself.

4.   in the clothes you wear.

3

Are tense people easily insulted?

yes

Those who think that happiness resides in
others' opinions - can/can't - easily be hurt
by the expression of these opinions.

can

If you know that happiness is inside you,
can you be easily insulted?

no

Is your inner state of relaxation changed
by someone's words?

It shouldn't be.
You're capable
of controlling it.

If a person doesn't like you (i. e. shows that
he is full of tension and rage) that's

1. your problem.

2. his problem.   2

A person who behaves toward you in a hostile
fashion is really expressing

1. his reaction to your inadequacy.

2. his own sickness.

A person's hostility concerns you only if it
makes you become offended, tense or enraged.
But when you lose control, such a person has in
a sense triumphed over you. He has succeeded
in making you as sick as he is. Can another
person insult you if you refuse to be insulted?   no

A would-be insult does you damage only when
you allow it to make you tense. A high level
of insultability shows that you are giving other
people the control over your body which you
yourself should possess.

If you refuse to become tense or unhappy, will
you find yourself in tense or unhappy situations?   no

Do all of your tensions exist within yourself?   yes

If you let other people control your reactions,
will you often become tense?   yes

If you are in complete control of your own
reactions, can the words or attitudes of
other people harm you?   no

BACK TO MR. BIGG'S OFFICE

As you may remember, Mr. Bigg has an over-
worked personal secretary named Jane McDermott.
Each day Mr. Bigg dictates a vast number of
memos. Jane receives no precise instructions
as to where the memos are to be sent, who is
to receive copies, etc. All this is left to her
own good sense. For several years she has
processed the memos without ever making a
serious mistake.

Today Mr. Bigg calls Jane into his office. He
informs her that she has sent the sales manager
a copy of a confidential memo in which he is
severely criticized. Furthermore, she has sent
another copy of this same memo to a competitor
who will find its contents very useful.

The letter which the competitor should have
received was sent to one of Mr. Bigg's rivals
in another branch of the company. It contained
information which could cost Mr. Bigg a
forthcoming promotion. He launches into a
tirade against "Miss McDermott's idiocy."

From our point of view, Miss McDermott's
most appropriate reaction at this point is
probably to

1. burst into tears.

2. take a deep breath and relax while Mr.
   Bigg talks himself out and she finds
   out what has really happened as a
   consequence of her error.

3. insist that Mr. Bigg is treating her
   unjustly.

4. leave the room.

5. resign.   2

Instead of doing any of these things, Jane
interrupts Mr. Bigg and gives him a long
explanation of why none of this could have
happened. She hasn't listened long enough
to find out that he already has the facts and
knows that it <u>did</u> happen. Would you suspect
that Jane succeeds in further enraging Mr.
Bigg?

She certainly
does.

When Jane finally finds out what the facts of
the situation are, she defends her mistake by
explaining how absurdly difficult her task is,
and how often she has to guess how many copies
of the memos to make and to whom she should
send them. In her opinion she proves conclusively
that Mr. Bigg is entirely to blame for the blunder.

As soon as Jane realized what had actually
happened, she should probably have

1. blamed everything on the sales
    manager.

2. admitted her mistake and apologized.

3. refused to type any more memos.

2

Jane's insistence that Mr. Bigg is at fault
will simply

1. calm him.

2. make him see the justice in her case.

3. improve his methods of dictation.

4. further enrage him.

4

Miss McDermott's rhetorical skill serves to
get her fired. When she sees what she has
done, she apologizes profusely, declaring
that the whole incident was her fault, and
swearing that it will not happen in the future
if Mr. Bigg will give her another chance.

By this time Mr. Bigg is feeling certain inner
reservations about discharging Miss McDermott,
because he knows that he is depriving himself
of an excellent secretary. But he feels that if
he abandons the stand he has taken he will lose
face before her and before others in the office
who would necessarily hear about the incident.
He therefore insists that she collect her two
week's pay and leave at once.

If Mr. Bigg were relaxed enough to think
clearly he would

1. devote more time to demonstrating
    Miss McDermott's incompetence.

2. promise never to write another memo.

3. admit that he is an incompetent tyrant
    and that it is all his fault.

4. accept Miss McDermott's apology and
    give her another chance.   4

He would realize that when he discharged Miss
McDermott he was thinking mainly of

1. his opinion of her.

2. her opinion of him.

3. his need for a good secretary.

4. his hatred of the sales manager.   2

In this case Mr. Bigg's attempt to preserve a
picture of himself in his secretary's eyes has

1. prevented any further mistakes in
    mailing.

2. made Miss McDermott a better secretary.

3. cost him an excellent secretary.

4. saved his time and his temper.   3

If Miss Mc Dermott herself had been somewhat
more relaxed, she might have let Mr. Bigg have
his say, admitted that she had made a mistake,
and then asked that he help her to prevent such
mistakes in the future by indicating where each
memo should be sent. This relaxed approach to
the situation might have preserved her job and
resolved a situation which had long been difficult.
Would she thus have done both herself and her
boss a favor?   yes

If Mr. Bigg had been capable of practicing
progressive relaxation during Miss McDermott's
reply, or even of drawing a few deep breaths
and repeating the word <u>relax</u> to himself, he
might have remained sufficiently objective to
see that firing her would gain him nothing, while
costing him an excellent secretary. Carried
away by his rage, he was thinking only of

1. his secretary's welfare.

2. his own welfare.

3. the role he was playing.   3

During this entire incident, both people were
so tense that they were conscious solely of

1. the necessity of preserving their own
    internal states of relaxation and
    happiness.

2. the necessity of telling the truth.

3. the necessity of protecting and
    justifying themselves.

4. the necessity of seeing the other person's
    point of view.

5. the necessity of changing their method
    of processing memos.   3

A tense person is caught up in the world of other
people's opinions.   In trying to maintain his
public image, he often takes actions which serve
no good purpose and cause him considerable harm.
Paradoxically enough, such actions ordinarily

1.   increase his importance in the eyes
     of other people.

2.   make him lose stature in the eyes of
     other people.   2

But this is not the most important loss in such
a situation.   A man's primary goal should be
his own happiness, which he can maintain only
by remaining relaxed and in control of himself.

In firing Jane, has Mr. Bigg behaved in a manner
conducive to his own happiness?   no

In defending herself to a point where she lost her
job, did Jane contribute to her own happiness?   no

AT HOME WITH THE BIGGS

Mr. Bigg has bought a wrist watch as a present
for his nine-year-old son John.   When John
comes home from the playground to get ready for
dinner, Mrs. Bigg tells him to go into the study
because his father wants to see him.

Unfortunately, these are the words which Mrs.
Bigg always uses when John is to be punished.
Furthermore, the study is always the site of
the punishment.

John is sure that he has done something wrong
and that his father is going to punish him.
Instead of going to the study, he runs and hides
in his room.   Mrs. Bigg finds him there, tells
him he's a bad boy to keep his father waiting,
and drags him off to the study.   By this time
John is already sniveling.

If John weren't so tense, he might try to
find out what he has done wrong, and thus
give his mother an opportunity to reassure
him. Would this response seem to be more
appropriate than hiding in his room?   yes

For her part, Mrs. Bigg is too tense to
find out what is troubling the boy. Instead
she adopts a forbidding attitude which
confirms his original suspicion that he is
to be punished.

We live in the worlds that we perceive.
Many people cannot relax sufficiently to
find out what is really happening in a
situation. Will such people tend to have   The probability
tense children?   of this is high.

If we meet a tense child, might we guess   As we have seen
that the people he lives with are also tense?   previously,
                                                  there is a good
                                                  probability that
                                                  this is the case.

Tension communicates itself. When we are
with tense people we tend to be _____.   tense
If we have to spend long periods of time with
them, we remain tense even after they have
left us.

Is relaxation as easily communicated?   yes

If we meet a very relaxed child, our
initial assumption is that his parents
are - tense/relaxed.   relaxed

THE WORLDS IN OUR HEADS

Let's return to the case of Mr. Bigg's son.
Mr. Bigg is amazed to see the boy arrive in
tears. Hoping to calm him, Mr. Bigg says,
"John, I have something here which I think
you deserve. " He has used similar words
when about to administer a spanking. John's
tears are transformed into wails of anguish.

Mr. Bigg feels that he has been unjustly
treated. As he sees the situation, he has
called the boy in to give him a present and
has received screams in exchange for his
kindness. He tells John to shut up. John's
screams redouble in volume. It might have
been wiser for Mr. Bigg to

1. buy no presents for the boy.

2. calm John and ask why he was crying.

3. send John out of the study in disgrace.

4. blame everything on Mrs. Bigg.   2

But tense people tend to overreact to a situation
as they immediately perceive it, without trying
to find out what is happening in other people's
heads. Mr. Bigg fancied himself in the role of
the generous parent. He feels that John has
gratuitously insulted him and rejected his gift.
He tells the boy to be quiet if he knows what's
good for him.

John is now completely unable to control himself.
Mr. Bigg finally spanks him and sends him away
without mentioning the watch. He tells Mrs. Bigg
that he wishes she could do something about "that
ungrateful cub. " He is so upset over the incident
that he is unable to continue working.

Would all three of the participants in this little
drama have suffered less if any one of them had
been able to relax long enough to find out what
was happening?   yes

Mr. Bigg has always said that he wanted to
mold his son in his own image. Has he
succeeded better than he knows?   yes

In the unlikely case that the three members
of the Bigg family were familiar with the
technique of progressive relaxation, would
this have been a good time to practice it?   yes

Note that progressive relaxation is a good
preventative if you are in sufficient control
· of yourself to practice it before you react to
a situation with rage and hostility. It is also
the best antidote after you have lost control
of yourself.

In the latter case, review the situation once
you are relaxed, analyze the mistakes that
you have made, decide on the best way to
rectify them, and remind yourself to remain
_____ the next time that a similar   relaxed
situation occurs.

If you find that you have lost control of
yourself, should you berate yourself for
your behavior and wallow in feelings of
guilt?   no

Calling yourself names only - raises/lowers -   raises
your level of tension.

If you are about to enter into a situation which
has previously caused you to become tense, you
may use your techniques of relaxation

   1.   only before entering the situation.

   2.   only during the situation.

   3.   only after the situation.

   4.   before, during, and after the
        situation.   4

MAKING DECISIONS

In our society many people become very
tense when they are faced with the task of
making a decision. They weigh various
alternatives, and sometimes find that all
solutions seem bad.

A person may hang on the horns of a dilemna
for weeks, months, or even years before he
finally forces himself to take some sort of
action. Even after reaching a decision, he
may continue to worry; often he feels that the
decision was bad, and regrets not having chosen
some other alternative.

Does it seem likely that there is something
wrong with a view of life which sees <u>all</u>
alternatives as <u>bad</u>?   Yes, indeed.

Let's see what we mean by <u>bad</u>. John Dalton
would say that a thing was bad only if he let
it make him unhappy. As we have already
learned, relaxation and tension, happiness
and unhappiness, are

   1.   found only within ourselves.

   2.   properties of external things.

   3.   the results of situations which
         occur in the outside world.   1

Your reactions are not in the outside world.
They are within you and can be controlled by
you. It is therefore not the type of external
situation in which you find yourself that matters,
but only the way in which you allow yourself to
perceive the outside world.

An external situation is bad only when

1. it causes us to lose money.

2. we feel it is bad and allow it to harm us.

3. other people think it is bad.   2

"Tense situations" are those which we permit

1. to make us happy.

2. to attract us.

3. to make us tense.   3

If you can remain relaxed and happy throughout the period which precedes the making of a decision, throughout the act of making the decision itself, and throughout the pursuit of the alternative which you have adopted, would John Dalton say that you have made a successful decision?   yes

The amount of happiness which results from a person's decisions is dependent upon

1. how well he has thought out all alternatives.

2. the wisdom of his choice.

3. the attitude of the person.   3

Let's examine some concrete examples of the results of decisions:

BUYING A NEW CAR

Joan and Helen have just graduated from
school, taken jobs, and decided to buy
cars. At first neither feels that she can
afford a new car.

But Joan's brother explains the troubles
which a woman can have with a second-hand
car, the annoyances caused by breakdowns,
the expense of repairs, and the ways in which
a person who knows nothing about cars can be
cheated. Some of her friends also tell of their
troubles with older cars.

Joan finally decides to buy a new foreign car,
and pay for it over a period of three years.
It has taken her three unhappy months of
constant worrying and balancing alternatives
to make this decision. During this time
her lack of a car has made getting to work difficult
and shopping inconvenient.

For some people, buying a new car is a very
pleasant experience. Did Joan seem to enjoy
the period in which she was making her decision?   no

Might she have enjoyed it if she had taken a
more relaxed attitude toward her purchase
and worried less about its consequences?   yes

Instead of enjoying her new car, Joan spends
her time berating herself for her inability to
understand some of its mechanical features,
for not having chosen a cheaper model or a
used car, for having financed the car so
foolishly that she has to pay too much interest,
etc. From our point of view, Joan has made a
bad decision because

1.   she bought a foreign car.

2.   she bought a new car.

3.   she didn't buy a used car

4.   she was overcharged for the financing.

5.   she was tense and unhappy before she
     bought the car, during the transaction,
     and afterwards.   5

BUYING AN OLD CAR

Joan's friend Helen makes the opposite decision.
She reasons that, since she can't afford a new
car, a second-hand one, however bad, is better
than no car at all. For several weeks she devotes
all her spare time going from one used car lot to
another.

During this time Helen develops a great distaste
for used-car salesmen and the ways in which she
feels they try to cheat her. Finally she chooses
a very old model because it is such a "good buy."
Immediately after making the down payment Helen
is sickeningly aware of having made a mistake.

Did it take Helen a long time to reach a
decision?   yes

Did she enjoy the whole process of decision-
making?   no

Did she finally choose a car which she really
wanted?   no

During the first few months, the second-hand
car has numerous breakdowns. It leaves Helen
stranded in improbable spots and requires frequent
and costly repairs. She reproaches herself for
not having known enough to buy a new car, and her
hatred of the old one increases rapidly.

Helen worries constantly about odd noises in her
car's engine and suspension, and about the high
cost of repairs. She complains loud and long to
her friends that she has been sold "a lemon."

Was Helen relaxed and comfortable with herself
during the period preceding or following the
purchase of her car?   no

Does she seem to enjoy the car?   no

Let's compare Helen's experiences in car
buying with those of two more of her girl
friends:

BUYING A SPORTS CAR

As she walks past a used-car lot, Charlotte
falls in love with a second-hand sports car.
Without asking herself whether she can afford
it, she buys it the same day. She immediately
baptizes it Phoebe and has a wonderful time
showing it off to her friends.

Was Charlotte tense and unhappy before she
made her decision or while she was making it?   no

Actually Charlotte might have spent less
money for a car which ran considerably
better than Phoebe, but she never considered
this at all. She loved the car and enjoyed
every experience with it, including the
interesting things she learned when it needed
repairs.

From our point of view Charlotte made a
successful purchase because

1. she spent so much time in
    comparative shopping.

2. she remained relaxed and happy both
    before and after buying the car.

3. she bought a second-hand sports car.

4. her car required few repairs.

5. she didn't buy a new car.   2

BUYING A BIG CAR

Ann earns a lower salary than any of our
other three car buyers, but she has always
wanted a big, new, luxury car. She doesn't
ask herself whether she can afford it, whether
she needs so large a car, or whether she
really "should" buy a smaller car. As soon as
she has the down payment, she buys her dream
car and drives happily away with it. She spends
every spare moment in her car and finds that it
has added a whole new dimension to her life.

Before she bought her car, was Ann tortured
by the necessity of making a decision?   no

Did she regret her decision after she bought
the car?   no

Which of the other girls does she resemble
in this respect?   Charlotte

Ann and Charlotte bought

  1. the same type of car.
  2. vastly different cars.   2

Nevertheless, from our point of view, the
two girls have much in common. They didn't
regret their choices or waste time thinking of
the cars they might have bought. Each remained
relaxed and happy while purchasing her car and
while using it afterward.

If happiness is your goal, your emotional
outlook is - more/less - important than   more
any specific decision you make.

How much you enjoy your car depends primarily
on

1. the type of car you buy.

2. your attitude toward your purchase.   2

From an objective viewpoint, some decisions are
better than others. But almost any decision is
a good one if you view it as such. Similarly, any
decision can be bad if you spend your time
regretfully wishing that you had made some
other choice. Might we say that the tension
which accompanies regret is always useless?

Most readers
have agreed that
it is silly to
torture yourself
with regrets.

Many people feel that regretting a "bad decision"
will help them to "learn from experience."
They thus think that their regret will benefit
them the next time that they have a decision to
make. Unfortunately it only serves to make
the next decision more difficult.

By castigating yourself for a bad decision, you
increase the anxiety associated with decision-
making. The end result is that each decision is
accompanied by so many fears that you invariably
categorize it as another mistake. Under such
circumstances no decision can bring happiness.

When you have a decision to make, you should
use your best judgment in selecting the
alternative

1. that other people tell you to choose.

2. that it seems will contribute most to
   your permanent happiness.   2

3. that involves the greatest amount of
   self-sacrifice.

If you find that you have made a mistake, and you are really dissatisfied with a decision, you should

1. spend your time regretting your choice.

2. use your best judgment to find an appropriate solution to the problem.

3. try to find someone to make your decisions for you.   2

Joan and Helen, the first two girls who bought cars, felt that they were prudently considering the various aspects of their situations. Actually they had both lost all sense of perspective. They had forgotten that their standard of living placed them in the upper five percent of the earth's population. Was there any danger of their starving to death as a result of an unwise purchase?   no

They were in danger of suffering only from

1. physical privation.

2. their own tensions and tension-induced self-recriminations.

3. unscrupulous salesmen.   2

Suppose that Joan and Helen had reversed their decisions. If Helen had bought a new foreign car and Joan an old second-hand one, would either of them have been happier?   probably not

The girl's primary goal should have been

1. finding the right kind of car.

2. saving as much money as possible.

3. remaining relaxed and happy.   3

BUYING NO CAR

Dick represents a more extreme example. He reads every automotive report for consumers, knows all the recommended models, and spends hours poring over the used-car ads in several newspapers. He tells himself that he will get a car whenever he finds the perfect buy. He has been looking for it now for ten years.

Dick seems to think that his only object
in buying a car should be

1. finding a model which he will
   enjoy.

2. finding the "perfect buy."

3. finding a car suited to his needs.   2

Dick's friends feel that he will probably visit
a psychiatrist before he ever reaches a car
lot. The purchase of a car should simply
contribute to his pleasure; Dick has made it
an end in itself. He is so tense and frightened
at the thought of making a mistake, that he will
almost certainly never buy a car at all.

Does this mean that all the time and energy
which Dick devotes to the study of cars is
wasted?   yes

Even without knowing anything further about
Dick, we would suspect that he

1. is very seldom relaxed and happy.

2. is a very relaxed person.

3. becomes tense only when thinking
   of cars.   1

M. D. OR NOT M. D.

Tom Jenkins, the son of a prominent brain
surgeon, is in his junior year at Bedford, a
small midwestern liberal arts college. Although
his natural inclination is toward English
literature, in accordance with his father's
wishes he is preparing to enter medical school.

Tom is taking a pre-med program because

1. he wants to study medicine.

2. he dislikes all other subjects.

3. his father wants him to study medicine.   3

Tom's father sent him to Bedford because of its strong pre-med program. In the past, the school has placed a number of students in medical school at the end of the junior year. At Bedford it has become traditional for all juniors in the pre-med program to send in applications to several medical schools.

Having long since sent in their applications, Tom's fellow students are now discussing their chances of acceptance at one school or another. For two months Tom has seized upon any excuse to push his application forms aside. His feeling of guilt has mounted steadily. This evening he has finally told himself that he must "get it over with."

Among the Bedford Juniors in the pre-med program, Tom is the - first/last - to fill out application forms for medical school.

last

Without knowing anything more about Tom, would you predict that he will fill out the application forms in short order, with a minimum of wasted effort?

It would seem unlikely.

Tom is applying to three medical schools. In addition to the usual vital statistics, they require him to state his reasons for having chosen medicine, and the contribution which he hopes to make to the profession. Tom has sought inspiration from medical texts and encyclopedias, but he can't seem to find any good reasons for studying medicine.

If Tom were really interested in medicine, he would find his reasons for studying it

1. in medical texts.

2. within himself.

3. in encyclopedias.

4. in his father's letters.

2

As he scribbles down one word and scratches
out another, Tom becomes increasingly aware
of the fact that his discomfort stems not so
much from the need to fill out application forms
as from the prospect of studying medicine. For
ten years he has successfully concealed his
dread of becoming a doctor. But now the day of
reckoning is no longer at a safe distance. With
frightening clarity Tom sees himself spending
years studying nothing but medicine, then
serving out his internship, and finally being
imprisoned in a doctor's office.

Does Tom seem pleased with the prospect of
medical school?   no

Does he want to become a doctor?   no

But Tom is equally unhappy at the thought of
becoming anything but a doctor. He tries to
imagine himself announcing a decision to major
in English to his father. He thinks of his
mother's disappointment. He hears the friends
of his family saying with a sneer, "The Jenkins
boy just didn't have it in him. "

As Tom considers abandoning a career in
medicine, foremost in his mind are

1. the opinions of his parents and
   their friends.

2. his own wishes.

3. his own limitations.   1

Tom can't stand the thought of being labelled
a quitter. Unable to face criticism, he
contemplates martyrdom. He tries to picture
himself as a prominent physician who has nobly
sacrificed his own happiness to serve the "good
of humanity. "

Is Tom in a position where he has to make a decision?

yes

Is he vacillating between two alternatives?

yes

Both alternatives seem - good/bad.

bad

Might this be an indication that there is something wrong with the way in which Tom has posed his problem?

yes

If you could see Tom at this moment, he would probably be

1. a picture of relaxation.
2. either hyperactive or rigid with tension.

2

Tom is the victim of anxieties which are

1. inherent in his choice of the medical profession.
2. necessarily associated with filling out application forms.
3. experienced by all people who have to make decisions.
4. inherent in his negative viewpoint.

4

Tom has not excelled in his pre-med courses, an unfortunate fact which adds considerably to his feelings of guilt and inadequacy. His high grades in English literature have afforded little comfort because they will not make a doctor of him. Tom has always felt that he had to choose a career worthy of his family's position in society.

Does choosing to scratch out a living as an English teacher seem compatible with the image which Tom feels he must maintain?

no

Suppose that instead of finding both alternatives
bad, Tom had difficulty in choosing between
them because they seemed equally attractive.
Would this be indicative of a healthier frame
of mind?   yes

Tom's negative attitude toward both alternatives
puts him in the position of deciding

    1.   which career he likes the most.

    2.   which career he finds the least
        distasteful.   2

Is a decision couched in negative terms
easy to make?   no

Tom will probably spend the night

    1.   torturing himself with doubts, fears
        and reproaches.

    2.   congratulating himself for having
        discovered where his abilities and
        interests lie.

    3.   planning to transfer from his pre-med
        courses to a department in which he
        will be more comfortable.   1

Will Tom have reached a definite decision
by morning?   probably not

Morning comes, and with it physiology class.
Tom squirms at his desk while the professor
expounds at length upon the dedication required
of a man of science.

Dr. Firth, a small nervous man with a tic, is
thinking of the experiment which he has just
concluded. He has only three days to revise
his notes for publication. When the bell rings
at the end of the class, he gathers up his papers
and prepares to scurry away to the laboratory.

Dr. Firth is unpleasantly surprised to find
his path barred by a distraught student.

"Yes?" Dr. Firth inquires with distaste.

Tom stammers for a moment and finally
manages to say, "I'd like to speak to you,
Sir; I have a problem."

Thinking longingly of his notes, but trying
to assume an expression of resignation, Dr.
Firth says, "Well, young man, out with it!"

Are both participants in the forthcoming
interview perfectly relaxed?   no

Does it seem likely that the interview will
resolve all of Tom's problems?   no

Facing this man of science, who could be
instrumental in getting him into medical
school, Tom feels his courage ebbing away.
He starts with, "Dr. Firth, I've been thinking..."

"Yes, yes, what is it?" interrupts Dr. Firth
impatiently. "Do you want a recommendation?"

"No, Sir," says Tom. "That is, yes, Sir. I
mean, I really don't know, Sir..."

"Don't know?" snaps Dr. Firth. "What is it
you don't know? What are you trying to say,
young man?"

Dr. Firth's impatience

1. will put Tom at ease.

2. will help Tom to express his real feelings.

3. will make Tom say anything to justify the
   demand he has made on his teacher's time.   3

Instead of explaining his real problem, Tom
finds himself concealing the fact that he doesn't
want to be a doctor. He has suddenly realized
that Dr. Firth won't be sympathetic toward a
student who wavers between going to medical
school and teaching English. In an effort to
fabricate a problem more likely to be received
favorably, he dwells at length on his doubts
concerning his ability.

Tom misstates his case so successfully that
Dr. Firth is left with the impression that his
student wishes to be told that the road to a
medical degree is paved with roses.

This is Dr. Firth's only free morning hour.
He is desperately eager to get back to his
notes. He expresses his hostility toward
Tom in the form of an attack on mediocrity.
He insists that the good medical schools
accept only courageous, gifted, selfless
young men burning with a passion for truth;
if Tom wants to be counted among the chosen
few, he'd better, "Shape up, and fast."

Is either participant in this interview
expressing his real problem or trying to
cope with it?   no

If Dr. Firth had been more relaxed, might
he have started by trying to find out what
was really troubling Tom?   yes

Might he then have made a more positive
contribution to the discussion?   yes

Did Tom's own state of tension prevent him
from telling Dr. Firth the truth?   yes

In misstating his case to Dr. Firth, Tom was

1. trying to put his problem as simply as possible.

2. trying to project a favorable image of himself to divert the hostility he had aroused.

3. trying to conceal the fact that he had any problems at all.   2

If Dr. Firth was relaxed enough to express his own wishes clearly, he might

1. explain why he hates students.

2. offer to devote his day to solving Tom's problem.

3. ask Tom to come back at a more convenient time.   3

Tom is stung by Dr. Firth's criticism. Reacting in defense of the very self-image that he was trying to abandon, he says, "I imagine that any student who applies to medical school has a few misgivings."

"You're a long way from medical school, my boy," replies Dr. Firth. "And you won't get there on the strength of your father's name. Your work in physiology could stand some improvement. That's where you'd better start right now. Your father could tell you that."

Continuing in this vein, Dr. Firth conjures up a vision of Tom stranded on the sands of mediocrity: "With second-rate grades, you'll be lucky to get into a second-rate medical school. If you get through at all, you'll be a second-rate doctor. There's no place in science for second raters. Now is the time to make up your mind," he concludes, rustling his papers meaningfully. "If you don't have the stuff, you'd better get out before you waste more of your parents' money and your teachers' time."

"Yes Sir, " Tom mutters disconsolately as
Dr. Firth takes his leave.

Dr. Firth's words probably leave Tom with
the feeling

1. that he has very little aptitude for
medicine.

2. that he can't possibly change his major
without branding himself as a loser.

3. that he is an awkward fool.

4. that he can obviously never be a
first-rate anything.   all four

Often we see a problem clearly only when we
have succeeded in communicating it to another
person. Did Tom's interview help him to state
his problem for himself?   no

Did Dr. Firth help Tom in any way?   no

Did he contribute materially to Tom's
distress?   yes

As a student of relaxation, how do you think
Tom should try to view his recent interview?

1. As ill-timed and unfortunate, but
not important enough to upset him.

2. As a bitterly truthful commentary on
his ineptitude, pronounced by a
powerful authority figure.

3. As proof of the fact that no one will
ever be able to understand his plight.   1

From what you know of Tom, would you guess   All readers
that the interview upset him?   answered yes.

Basic to all of Tom's problems is the fact that

1. he doesn't want to be a doctor.
2. he wants to be an English teacher.
3. he's afraid of his father.
4. he doesn't realize that he has a right
   to take personal happiness as his primary
   goal.   4

Tom now sees himself as a desperate man. As
he passes the administration building, he has a
momentary impulse to try to see the Dean. But
the interview with Dr. Firth is still fresh in his
mind. Another such experience would be too
painful to endure.

Tom goes to his room, but there the application
forms await him. He hurries back to the
administration building.

As a person's level of tension rises, he

1. is better able to plan his life.
2. acts less and less rationally.   2

Dr. Jones, Dean of the College, is a very busy
man. Nevertheless he remains relaxed and
cheerful throughout the day. As a result, he is
well liked by both students and faculty. A personal
friend of Tom's father, Dr. Jones himself urged
the boy to select the most difficult pre-med courses.

Seeing Tom hovering nervously near his door,
Dr. Jones invites him in.

"Do you have a moment?" Tom asks.

"All the time in the world," the Dean replies.
"What can I do for you?"

Suddenly Tom feels better. Deciding on a quick plunge into the icy waters, he blurts out, "I think I'd like to change my major."

For Tom's sake, we hope that Dr. Jones answers,

1. "I wonder what your father would say to that?"

2. "Do you realize what a serious thing that is for a junior to be considering?"

3. "I think it can be arranged. What did you have in mind?"

4. "Someday you'll change your mind once too often, young man!"   3

Fortunately for Tom, the Dean is a student of relaxation. He not only responds appropriately, but leads Tom to talk of his interest in English literature. Together they arrange a schedule which will permit Tom to graduate the following year as an English major. Feeling relaxed and comfortable for the first time, Tom ventures to ask the Dean's opinion concerning his change of major.

Since we know that Dr. Jones is a relaxed person, we would expect him to say

1. "I think you're making a serious mistake."

2. "This will break your father's heart."

3. "If you really want to change your major, it's the only sensible thing to do."   3

Once again the Dean chooses the appropriate response. Breathing an enormous sigh of relief, Tom says, "I'm glad to hear that you approve, Sir."

"Why?" asks Dr. Jones. "What difference does my opinion make?"

"Well, "answers Tom, "everyone seems to want me to be a doctor." He thinks for a moment and then adds, "Especially my father."

For the first time, Dr. Jones appreciates the full extent of the boy's problem. He says, "If your father is the sane man that I think him to be, he will want you to

1. become a doctor at all costs."

2. consider the family first in your choice of a career."

3. sacrifice yourself to humanity."

4. consider your own happiness as the primary factor in any decision." 4

We must hope that Dr. Jones is correct in his appraisal of Tom's father. But Tom's high level of tension indicates that his father is probably

1. an extremely relaxed man.

2. a somewhat tense individual. 2

After his interview with Dr. Jones, Tom rushes happily off to communicate his decision to his favorite English professor. Did he derive any benefit from the anguish which accompanied the first phases of his decision? no

If Dr. Jones had been an anxiety-ridden man, would he have communicated his tension to Tom? yes

In that case, would the interview have been likely to give Tom the positive help he sought? no

If Tom were as relaxed as Dr. Jones, would
he need to call on someone else to make his
decisions for him?   no

If Tom maintains his present level of tension
is he likely to have further attacks of anxiety
concerning his change of career?   yes

If Tom's father adopts a hostile attitude toward
the boy's decision, will Tom be able to withstand
criticism without suffering tension and guilt?   probably not

On the other hand, if his father is pleased with
Tom's decision, will all of Tom's problems be
permanently solved?   probably not

Unless Tom becomes considerably more
_____, undue tension will accompany   relaxed
every decision he has to make.

If he is to enjoy his life, Tom must learn that

1.   his happiness depends upon the career
     which he chooses.

2.   other people can make his decisions
     for him.

3.   he must always try to please everyone.

4.   a person who does what he wants, while
     remaining relaxed and happy, will tend
     to make "good decisions."   4

It has been instructive for us to examine the
mistakes of others, but eventually we must
apply what we have learned to our own lives.

Let's see how well you can avoid similar errors
in the following situations:

THE MAJESTY OF THE LAW

You are driving along a section of highway
on which the speed limit drops to 50 miles
an hour. You are doing 65 and just keeping
up with traffic.

A policeman pulls up beside you and waves
you over to the side of the road. After you
pull off, he stops his car up the road and
starts walking back toward you.

Since you assume that the policeman will
ask for your license and registration, you
pull them out. You haven't had much
practice with progressive relaxation, and
you feel that you don't have time to try it.
Suggest some techniques which you might
practice during the short period which it
will take the policeman to reach your car.

Close your eyes,
breathe deeply,
and repeat the
word relax.
(Smiling, yawning
and stretching
might also be
practiced while
the policeman
is still at some
distance.)

As a result of a series of unfortunate experiences
with authority figures, from fathers to army
sargeants, most men in our society have a fear of
the policeman which is out of all proportion to the
amount of discomfort which he can cause. While
you are relaxed, it is well to remind yourself that
the policeman can do you no physical harm, that a
fine of a few dollars won't matter at all, and that
you can do yourself real damage by becoming tense.

The policeman's initial gem is, "Look, Mac, have
you ever driven a car before?"

You answer by saying

1. "No, but isn't it fun!"

2. "Yes, but it's the first time I've had to swerve to avoid being run down by a police car."

3. "Yes, I've been driving for 14 years (or however many it happens to be)."

4. "Yes, and I'll thank you not to make any more insolent remarks."

5. "Yes, but I've never run anyone off the road."

3
(The other replies all indicate that you are unwisely trying to impress the policeman and yourself with false bravado.)

The policeman continue, "Do you happen to have a driver's license?"

You answer by saying

1. "Yes, do you?"

2. "I don't need a license; I'm only 12 years old."

3. "Why no, what do you charge for them?"

4. "Here it is."

5. "Yes, I just happened to find this one in my wallet."

4
(Again, any other answer gives the policeman more importance than he deserves. You don't need to act for him.)

Throughout this entire proceeding, your goal remains that of staying relaxed and comfortable with yourself. You should not try to cut a dashing figure in the eyes of the policeman, or grovel before him in the hope of avoiding a ticket.

It is better to pay for a $12 ticket than to spend hours in a state of tension caused by fear and rage. Might you even find that you are less likely to get a ticket when you are relaxed?

This has been the experience of many people. But avoiding the ticket should not be your primary goal.

After you have also handed the policeman
your registration, he says, "All right, Joe,
do you know you are doing 75 in a 50-mile-
an-hour zone?"

You reply

1. "I wasn't doing a mile over 65."
2. "I didn't realize that."
3. "I was barely keeping up with traffic.
   Why don't you arrest the whole world?"
4. "Aren't freeways exciting?"
5. "I didn't see any signs."
6. "How fast were you going when you
   ran me down?"   2

The policeman continues, "Well, buddy, I
should give you a ticket, but this time I'm
going to let you off with a warning."

You say

1. "How about them (pointing at the
   cars whizzing by)?"
2. "Gee thanks, God."
3. "Don't do me any favors."
4. "Thank you."
5. "I'll mention your kindness to the
   governor."   4

The policemany says, "You'd better be thankful
that I'm in a good mood today. Take it easy,
and obey the speed limits, you hear?"

You say

1. "If you weren't hiding behind that uniform, I'd show you what sort of mood I'm in."

2. "I'm so grateful I could cry."

3. "Fine. I'll do that."

4. "Thank you very much officer, you've been wonderful."

5. "If I tried to hold my speed down to 50 on this track, I'd be crumpled up like an accordion."   3

In such a situation, the only important happenings take place

1. in the policeman's mind.

2. inside of you.

3. in the policeman's notebook.

4. in your exchange of glances.

5. in your understanding of the law.   2

If, in spite of your reminders to yourself, the policeman has succeeded in making you tense, practice progressive relaxation for a few minutes before continuing your drive.

When you do return to the highway, keep a smile on your face and practice the other appropriate techniques of relaxation. They will prevent you from spending all your time looking for other policemen.

DINING OUT

You are taking your family out to dinner.
You don't bother to call and make a
reservation, because it is a weekday night
and you know that the restaurant you have
chosen is seldom crowded.

You are greeted by a blond receptionist who
asks if you have a reservation. You can see
that the restaurant is practically empty. You
say to the receptionist

    1.   "What do you mean, reservation? This
        dump is empty."

    2.   "We have no reservation."

    3.   "We've never needed a reservation
        before on a weekday night."

    4.   "If you want to play games, we'll try
        another restaurant."   2

The receptionist says "would you please take
a seat in the lounge for a moment while I speak
to the Maitre d' (fantastically mispronounced)."

You reply

    1.   "You'd be a whiz in a French class."

    2.   "Peroxide, you've just lost a customer."

    3.   "We'd rather go somewhere else than
        wait for any length of time."

    4.   "We'll wait as long as you wish."

3
(If you find it
necessary to be
either insolent
or subservient
to a receptionist
in a restaurant,
your tension
level is mounting.
So much respect
for her opinion
is unwarranted.
You should feel
no need to act
for her.)

Seated in the comfortable chairs in the lounge, you have a good chance to remind yourself that your goal is to remain relaxed and happy. In your conversation, you

1. discuss the low cultural level of the receptionist.

2. make slighting remarks about this particular restaurant.

3. attack all restaurants for the annoyances which attend the whole process of eating out.

4. remark that the lounge is very comfortable and that you are looking forward to a good meal.   4

Ten minutes pass and the receptionist fails to return. This would seem to be the time to

1. stamp out with a great show of anger.

2. find the receptionist and give her a piece of your mind.

3. find a more congenial restaurant.

4. ask to see the manager and do what you can to get the receptionist fired.

5. try to convince yourself that you are not very hungry.   3

You walk out

1. as fast as you can.

2. bristling with indignation and making loud remarks about the service.

3. slowly and calmly.

4. with contemptuous glances at all and sundry.

5. growling at the receptionist.   3

You go next door to a new restaurant which
you have never tried before. As it turns out,
the food is excellent, but the service is very
slow. You spend two hours eating and talking
of

1. how much you hate the receptionist
   next door.

2. how disgusted you were with the first
   restaurant you visited.

3. how good the food is and how much you
   are enjoying your evening.

4. how slow the service is.

5. how bad all restaurants are.   3

When going out for the evening, it is well to
remain relaxed enough to keep your objectives
clearly in mind. If your primary goal is that
of enjoying yourself, you will not want to spoil
your evening by accumulating or doling out ego
bruises, or by complaining about the various
indignities to which you feel you have been
submitted.

Realize that you are going to come in contact
with many people whose views may differ from
yours, and that you will only enrage yourself
and them if you spend your time trying to teach
them lessons. Leave injustice-collecting to the
masochists whose goal is to suffer as much as
possible.

A BIG DECISION

You have been working for six years as an
accountant in a large corporation. One of your
colleagues has decided to go into business for
himself. He offers you the position of business
manager in his new company. You have a week
to make your decision.

Your boss knows of your dilemma. He
undertakes to advise you, and points out
the following things:

(1) Your present salary is higher than
the one which you have been offered.

(2) If you leave, you will lose your
contributions to the retirement plan.

(3) You will not be able to afford the new
car that you have promised your wife.

(4) You will no longer be assured of
regular pay raises.

(5) The majority of small businesses fail
in the first two years.

(6) The bankruptcy of the new company
would leave you without a job.

(7) You do not have to work long hours
on your present job, and you are
spared the elementary drudgery of
bookkeeping that you will have with
a small concern.

The boss sums it all up by saying that, while
you have almost perfect security in your
present position, there is a real possibility
of failure in the new job. He also reminds you
that your present job offers group insurance,
hospitalization, and many other fringe benefits
which you will not have with a smaller organization. He points out that your salary permits you
to make regular contributions to a college plan
for your children. In his opinion, you would be
foolish to abandon the security offered by your
present position for a very uncertain future.

You have been reminding yourself to remain
relaxed throughout this entire period of
decision-making. You tell your boss

1. to mind his own business.

2. that when you need his advice
   you will ask for it.

3. that he has convinced you that you
   ought to stay with him.

4. that you think you will have more
   security in the new company.

5. that you are grateful for his advice
   and will certainly consider it as you
   weigh alternatives and make your
   decision.   5

You talk the matter over with your wife. She
also feels that your present job offers you
greater security.

You explain to your wife that a "secure job"
doesn't necessarily make for a feeling of
personal security, and that no job is in itself
a guarantee of happiness. You point out that
your objective in life is not to find a safe niche
in a large organization, but to insure your own
personal happiness. You add that

1. a person is insecure only if he feels
   insecure.

2. hospital plans and insurance offer
   complete security.

3. old jobs are less secure than new
   jobs.

4. new jobs are less secure than old
   jobs.

5. you would feel more secure if you had
   your boss's job.   1

MORE ADVICE

The friend who has invited you to join him
in business gives you his advice. He feels
that the new position will offer the following
things:

(1) a chance to select your own working
associates.

(2) considerable novelty which is lacking
in your present work.

(3) an opportunity to be much more creative,
and to have the fun of setting up your own
world.

(4) the right to do things your own way, and
to correct the faulty accounting procedures
which you have criticized in your present
firm.

(5) the authority to make your own decisions,
instead of following orders which you
regard as silly.

(6) a considerable share of the stock of the
company and a place on the board of
directors.

(7) a possibility of becoming wealthy and thus
giving your family luxuries which you could
never afford in your present position.

You inform your colleague that

1. you are sure he's right and you will
take the job.

2. external working conditions are the most
important things in the world.

3. you feel that his job doesn't offer
sufficient security.

4. you are going to stay in your present job.

5. you feel that your happiness at work will
result more from an attitude that you bring
to the job than from any benefits which the
job can give you.   5

ENJOYING YOUR JOB

You then proceed to make your own
decision, without dramatizing it. You
don't pretend to decide on the basis of
what you feel you owe your wife and
children.

You have learned that when you are relaxed
and happy the people around you tend to feel
the same way. You therefore believe that the
greatest contribution you can make to the
members of your family is the full enjoyment
of your life with them.

You ask yourself whether you like your present
job, and you decide that you do. On the other
hand, you are sure that you will enjoy the new
job if you approach it in the correct frame of
mind. It is therefore a question only of what
you really want to do.

Your answer comes immediately without
any conscious feeling of wrestling with
various alternatives. You enjoy learning
new things and know that you will welcome
the experience of carving out a world for
yourself in a different situation. Without
further self-questioning, you realize that
your heart lies with the new job. You
have enough confidence in yourself not to
fear failure. Therefore you

1. owe it to yourself to choose the
   job which will offer you greater
   personal happiness

2. owe it to your wife and family to
   choose the job which will offer you
   more security.

3. owe it to your boss to dedicate your
   life to his firm.   1

Furthermore, having a share in a firm and
being largely responsible for its success or
failure seems to be a more interesting game
than the one you are playing at the moment.
The primary factor in your decision to accept
the new position is

1. the greater amount of money to be
made in the new job.

2. your own emotional well-being.

3. the brilliant future which the job
offers.

4. the greater sense of importance which
you attach to the new position.

5. your hatred of your old job.   2

As you leave for the new job, you reflect that

1. you are sure you've made the best
objective choice.

2. you really should have devoted an
anxious week to considering alternatives,
instead of acting hastily and risking a
mistake.

3. you should have asked for two more
weeks to make your decision.

4. as long as you remain relaxed and
comfortable with yourself, you can't
have made a mistake.   4

The sequel proves that you might have gained
more money and prestige by remaining in your
old job. After ill health forces your former
boss to retire, your successor is rapidly
promoted to the position of vice president
in charge of his division.

Meanwhile, you are instrumental in bringing
a moderate degree of success to your new
company, in which you also have the title of
vice president. In your spare moments it
seems appropriate to think of

1. how much you regret your decision to
   leave the old company.

2. how much money you could have made
   as vice president of a large firm.

3. how much you enjoy your present work.

4. how you wish you could find another
   new company and start over.

5. how much you hate your successor
   for having taken a place which might
   have been yours.   3

Often you also remind yourself that

1. you can never be relaxed in a big
   company.

2. it is impossible to be relaxed if you
   hold an executive position in a small
   company.

3. relaxation can be practiced only after
   working hours.

4. you are in control of your own body,
   and you can be as relaxed and happy
   as you decide to be; the only really
   important decision in life is to enjoy
   it.   4

Should all subsequent decisions be subordinate
to the goal of remaining in a relaxed state which
permits full enjoyment of every situation?   yes

DEALING WITH SICK DOCTORS

You are a nurse who has had an opportunity
to observe and record a series of very
interesting case histories. You have been
asked to give a report of your experiences
at a large national convention of doctors and
nurses.

You have had no recent experience in public
speaking, but in the years before you became
acquainted with the techniques of relaxation
you were always terrified at the prospect of
addressing even a small group.

When you did appear before an audience, you
were always so tense that you were not fully
conscious of what you did or said, and you were
equally unaware of the reactions of your listeners.
Your whole talk disappeared in a sort of blur, but
you were afterwards told that you had done
creditably.

This sort of compliment once left you with a
vague impression that the tension you felt
when you gave a speech was necessary to your
success. But the speaker who precedes you
seems to be relaxed; his presentation is
nonetheless very effective. You realize that
you succeeded previously in spite of your
tension rather than because of it. You decide
that

1. a high level of tension is necessary
    to the success of a lecturer.

2. an audience reacts better to a tense
    speaker.

3. both you and your audience will enjoy
    the experience much more if you can
    remain relaxed.

4. it is good for a speaker to become so tense
    that he can no longer monitor what he says.   3

The discussion period which follows the first
talk is drawing to a close, and you realize
that you will be on stage in about five minutes.
It will probably be most profitable for you to
spend those minutes

1. desperately rehearsing your speech

2. trying to find an exit.

3. telling yourself that you will just
    have to go through with it.

4. practicing progressive relaxation.   4

As you walk up to the platform, you remind
yourself that you will strive to remain in
relaxed control of yourself. This will permit
you to measure the effect of your words as you
deliver them. Your primary objective remains
that of

1. impressing the group with your
    brilliance.

2. getting through the speech.

3. remaining as relaxed and comfortable
    as possible during your delivery of the
    speech.

4. communicating as many facts as possible
    to your audience.   3

A secondary result of your relaxed delivery
will be

1. a growing hostility from your audience.

2. a highly favorable emotional reaction
    from the audience.

3. a marked tendency to daydream among
    the members of the audience.

4. a mass exit from the auditorium.

5. a tendency to put the audience to sleep.   2

Your relaxed attitude toward your subject
matter and yourself is reflected in a pleasant
tone of voice and a calm presentation free of
nervous mannerisms.

You do not make sweeping generalizations and
flat dogmatic assertions. You present the facts
of the case, giving due credit to everyone
concerned, and allowing the members of your
audience to draw their own conclusions.

You have reason to believe that some of the
delegates were hostile at the beginning of
your talk. When you finish your presentation,
you find that in most cases their antagonism
has

    1.   doubled.

    2.   decreased considerably.   2

But some people are so hostile that they launch
attacks against speakers who have seemingly
done nothing to provoke them. A delegate who
indulges in this type of criticism is really
expressing his own

    1.   high level of tension and unhappiness.

    2.   hatred of incompetent lecturers.

    3.   love of objective truth.   1

It is well to remember in such cases that
you are dealing with people who are

    1.   hostile only toward you.

    2.   hostile toward what you say.

    3.   full of general hostility.   3

Two doctors try to heckle you during the
question and answer period. In an accusing
tone the first points out that you have offered
only a simple description of your case histories,
without any controls to show what the results
might have been if other therapeutic methods
had been employed.

You reply that

1. he doesn't seem to have understood
   a word you said.

2. a series of more authoritative doctors
   than he decided that controls were
   unnecessary.

3. what he says is perfectly true, but you
   had not intended to conduct a controlled
   experiment of the type he describes.   3

The second doctor analyzes your use of various
technical terms and makes it apparent that he
thinks you lack the medical training necessary
to present a worthwile paper. The reactions
of other members of the audience indicate that
they consider his criticism to be completely
unwarranted. You tell him that

1. his rudeness seems to be equalled
   only by his encyclopedic ignorance.

2. you feel he has made a number of
   useful remarks, and you are sorry
   that he doesn't approve of your
   terminology; you have done your
   best to check it with leading authorities.

3. you didn't come here to be insulted by
   a maniac.

4. you are sorry that he is so sick, but you
   will have to answer those members of the
   audience who have questions relating to
   your talk.

5. he is at liberty to continue this discussion
   with some of the doctors who directed your
   work; they would seem to know more about
   these things than he.   2

A number of doctors in the audience rush to
your rescue. The debate tends to become
personal and vindictive. You decide to

1. help your rescuers to eliminate
   your critics.

2. prevent the critics from getting the floor
   by calling only on obvious supporters.

3. calm the entire group down by admitting
   that there is truth on both sides, and then
   ask for contributions from those who haven't
   been given a chance to speak.

4. terminate the discussion without letting
   anyone else speak.   3

You are notified that the time allotted to the
discussion period is almost up, and that you
have only three minutes left to summarize
what has been said. You use the three
minutes to

1. repeat your original arguments more
   forcefully.

2. sum up the arguments pro and con which
   have been expressed during the discussion
   period and thank everyone for shedding
   more light on the subject.

3. say that the discussion has been leading
   nowhere, and that it would have to be
   terminated anyway.

4. attack the arguments of those who
   assailed your presentation.

5. repeat only the comments of those
   who agreed with you.   2

As you sit listening to the next speaker, you find that in spite of all your precautions, you have become somewhat tense. You eliminate this tension by

1. discussing your performance with the person seated next to you, and trying to elicit compliments.

2. stepping outside to continue the discussion with a group of people who have also become tense, and insist on finishing the debate.

3. waiting for an opportunity to attack the next speaker.

4. practicing step-by-step relaxation while you listen to the next speaker.   4

SUMMARY

Decide whether each of the following statements is true or false:

1. In public speaking, as in all other situations in life, your primary goal is to relax and enjoy yourself.   true

2. You must have had the secondary goal of making a favorable impression on your audience, or you wouldn't have spoken at all.   true

3. Your primary goal of relaxing and enjoying yourself and your secondary goal of making a favorable impression are usually complementary.   true

4. Relaxation and enjoyment communicate themselves readily.   true

5. Tension is not easily communicated.   false

6. A tense speaker retains sufficient control of himself to monitor his remarks and the reactions of his audience.   false

7. A relaxed speaker can monitor his remarks and choose words which will neither insult his listeners nor demand that they agree with some arbitrary position which he has taken.   true

8. A tense person can keep clearly in mind
the fact that his secondary goal is not
proof of his own brilliance, but a favorable
reaction from his audience.   false

9. A calm, relaxed presentation will usually
win most members of your audience over
to your point of view.   true

10. If you remain relaxed, you will always get
a favorable reaction from all members of
your audience.   false

11. A few people are so hostile that they
criticize even the most relaxed speakers.   true

12. You should answer a hostile attack with an
even more hostile reply.   false

13. A calm and reasoned reaction to an unjusti-
fied attack will help you to maintain your
own relaxation and poise and also win most
of the audience over to your side.   true

DANGEROUS EGO PICTURES

An ex-serviceman of about average height and
weight, you are now employed as the assistant
manager of a bank. You and your wife have
gone dancing with some friends.

A group of tough-looking young men take a
nearby table. They begin drinking heavily
and staring over at your party. Suddenly one
of them gets up, comes over, and asks your
wife to dance. Her most appropriate response at
this point is to

1. say, "Scram, Junior."

2. say, "I'd love to, but my husband
won't let me."

3. say nothing and turn to you for help.

4. say, "No, thank you."

5. slap the young man across the face.   4

But your wife's reaction is not appropriate.
She becomes tense and frightened and turns
mutely to you for help. This is doing you no
great favor. Our social mores make the
possibility of her being physically injured by
a young thug quite remote, but they make the
probability of a conflict between you and him
relatively high.

Prudently you look for a waiter or a bouncer,
but no one is in sight. The junior Dillinger
continues, "Come on, Baby. Foureyes won't
mind." At this reference to your glasses,
you feel a mounting muscular tension, a danger
signal which you have learned to recognize.

In most situations in our society the physical
damage which you suffer from tension is only
internal. But your failure to remain relaxed
in this predicament may easily cause one or
more persons to be badly hurt or jailed.

If you allow yourself to be offended by the
term "Foureyes," and start a fight with the
young thug, you will have

1. proved that you can't be insulted.

2. allowed him to communicate his
    sickness and hostility to you.

3. made the situation much more
    comfortable for your wife.   2

If you remind yourself that happiness is an
internal thing which you control, you

1. can't be insulted by others' opinions.

2. will be ready to fight at the drop of
    a hat.   1

Reflecting on all this, you pause for a moment
and tell yourself to relax. But a member of
your party, a huge ex-paratrooper seated next
to your wife, is already on his feet. Your
friend has had a couple of drinks and is prepared
to release a few of his own tensions. "Get lost,
punk," he grunts none too amiably.

The young man takes a step backwards and
reaches into a pocket which may or may not
contain a weapon. His three friends leap to
their feet. This is a good time for you to

1. jump on the youth and pin his arms.

2. back up the ex-paratrooper.

3. scold your wife.

4. rally your other friends to attack
   the opposite table.

5. do something about stopping all this.   5

You step in between the antagon᠁ 's and explain
to the young man that your wife has promised
the next dance to your friend, indicating the
paratrooper. With a nod of your head you signal
to your wife to move the paratrooper off toward
the dance floor. You then walk the youth back
toward his table, explaining that

1. he may be badly hurt if he doesn't
   leave the place in a hurry.

2. you and your friends are all afraid
   of him.

3. none of you is looking for trouble, but
   the people at your table prefer to remain
   with their own party.

4. you wish he'd drop dead.

5. you can handle him and three more
   like him.

6. your wife would really love to dance
   with him.   3

The group at the other table calms down
momentarily. But they continue to drink
and cast glances in your direction. When
they again start making loud remarks and
gesturing toward your party, you suggest
to your friends that you might all enjoy the
evening more if you adjourned to another
spot.

The men at your table have been drinking.
Several of them insist angrily that they
are not afraid of a bunch of punks.

You therefore look for a waiter again and
are fortunate enough to find him this time.
You ask that he have a bouncer talk to the
young men.

The waiter says that he doesn't believe the
bouncer will do anything unless there is an
actual fight; even then, he doesn't know how
effective the bouncer will be, because he
may be afraid of this particular group.

This is the moment for you to

1. tell your friends that they will probably
   have a fight on their hands.

2. tell your group that your goal this
   evening is relaxation and enjoyment;
   therefore you and your wife are going
   to find a more congenial place.

3. go over to the other group and explain
   that they can have a fight if they want one.   2

It takes considerable training in self control
to remain relaxed during such an incident. It
is well to remember that your primary goal is

1. impressing your group with your
   courage.

2. impressing the other group with your
   courage.

3. impressing your wife with your courage.

4. impressing yourself with your courage.

5. your own enjoyment.   5

If you choose one of the first four alternatives,
you still think that happiness is somewhere
outside of you, and that you must earn it by
impressing other people. You may insist that
you are proving your own courage to yourself
and others, but you are really living up to the
standards which you believe the group admires,
even at the cost of your own happiness.

You - should/shouldn't - place your personal   shouldn't
happiness in others' hands.

In a "fighting situation, " a sane and relaxed
person remembers that the danger of real
trouble lies

1. in the situation.

2. in him.

3. in his antagonists.

4. in his friends.   2

Television's soldiers, cowboys and gangsters
have instilled suicidal reaction patterns in the
American male. Only a relaxed person can
process alternatives and calmly choose the
appropriate response to a difficult situation,
instead of reacting blindly in TV terms.
Many people who have yielded to mounting
waves of tension are now in cemeteries or
jails.

REMAINING RELAXED IN EVERYDAY SITUATIONS

We have cited some examples of tension-provoking
incidents because they permit you to distinguish
clearly between the appropriate responses, which
you make when you remain sufficiently relaxed to
process alternatives, and the _____   inappropriate
ones elicited from tense individuals.

But the situations which we face from day to day
are usually less dramatic, and therefore less
clear-cut. At any given moment most people
are far more tense than necessary. As we saw
in the case of Barry Stone, even individuals
working alone can become very tense; and most
of us become _____ when we work with other   tense
people.

Is a certain amount of tension always present
in muscles which are performing work?   yes

Such muscles should be tensed

1. as much as possible.

2. as little as possible.

3. just enough to perform the assigned task.   3

You will have reached the most advanced state of
relaxation when you are able to maintain the
minimum necessary amount of specific tension in
muscles which you are using, while allowing the
rest of your body to remain _____.   relaxed

We will now combine general relaxation with
the use of the minimum specific tension
required in a series of very common situations.

BASIC POSITIONS FOR RELAXATION

In the course of a 24-hour day, adults in our
society divide their time among three basic
body positions.

At least 8 hours should be spent lying down.
What fraction is this of the entire day?   1/3

We have already practiced the techniques of
relaxation to be used when lying down. Before
we discuss the second basic position, remind
yourself of the following facts:

Our skeletal and muscular structure permits
our bodies to be <u>completely</u> relaxed only when
we are ....   lying down

You - can/cannot - achieve complete relaxation   cannot
in any other position.

Therefore, in the interest of relaxation, you
- should/shouldn't - try to lie down for short
periods during the day.   should

If possible, have a couch available so that you
can lie down occasionally while you are at your
office or place of employment. If this is
impossible, practice relaxation in the other
positions which we are about to discuss, and
lie down for a brief period as soon as you
return home from work.

One caution should be mentioned here. Since
they know that it is easiest to relax when lying
down, many people make the mistake of thinking
that they should always lie down to read a book
or watch television. This is a serious error for
two reasons:

(1) Considerable strain is introduced when
you try to hold your head and neck in an
unnatural position to see a book or the
TV set.

More strain is occasioned by your concentration on what you see. Even though you
are lying down, it is - possible/impossible -   impossible
for you to relax completely.

(2) You gradually build up strong habits which
compete with your desire to relax. You
begin to associate the tension introduced
by the strain of holding your head up with
the position of lying down.

As a consequence, you no longer associate
lying down solely and completely with
_____ and sleep. You don't   relaxation
necessarily expect to relax completely
when you lie down, and soon you find that
it is harder and harder for you to fall
asleep.

For these two reasons, you should reserve the
position of lying down solely for relaxation and
_____ .   sleep

You will then find that you often fall asleep
when you lie down for brief periods of
relaxation during the day, and that you
wake up enormously refreshed.

RELAXING WHILE SITTING

The average American spends approximately
8 hours a day in a sitting position. Does this
mean that he sits for about the same length of
time that he spends lying down?   yes

We will therefore consider sitting to be our
second basic position. It differs from the
first position in several respects:

Is complete relaxation possible when you are
lying down?   yes

Is it possible when you are sitting?   no

Some muscular tensions are necessary in
order to hold your body in a sitting position.
The muscles of your neck are tensed to hold
your head up. The muscles of your back are
tensed sufficiently to keep you from falling.
Muscles hold up those parts of your arms
which are not completely supported. If your
feet are on the floor, a certain amount of
_____ necessarily exists in your feet and   tension
legs.

There is an added complication. You lie down
when you wish to do nothing but relax and sleep.
At that time you are not engaged in any sort of
activity. Are you usually doing something
or other when you are sitting down?   yes

While sitting, people in our society are
ordinarily engaged in some such activity as
eating, drinking, talking, reading, writing,
watching TV, listening to music, etc.
Usually their eyes are - open/closed.   open

Does this mean that some tension must exist
in the eye muscles?   yes

If a person is reading or writing, must he
tense the arm that holds the pencil or book?   yes

It will be your object to conduct the activities
which you perform while sitting down with a
- maximum/minimum - of general and specific   minimum
tension.

Certain tensions are appropriate to particular
activities. If you are conversing with someone,
will you need to tense the muscles of speech
sufficiently to move your tongue and lips?   yes

Will you need to hold your hands very tightly
clasped in your lap?   no

Tightly clasped hands would be an example of
an - appropriate/inappropriate - specific tension   inappropriate
in a conversational situation.

This type of inappropriate specific tension is
usually an indication of a - high/low - level   high
of general tension throughout the muscles of
the body.

Instead of keeping his hands clasped, a person
uses them to make unnecessary, rapid, darting
gestures. Might this also be an indication of a
high level of general tension?   yes

Suppose that a friend of yours speaks very
rapidly, in a high-pitched, shrill tone; he
rolls his eyes often, wrinkles his forehead,
and shifts position constantly. Is this behavior
indicative of tension?   yes

While sitting and conversing with others, we can
use the above clues to decide whether or not we
have succeeded in relaxing. Before practicing
relaxation in this relatively difficult situation,
let's start with an easy example.

RELAXING WHILE WATCHING TV

Suppose that you are about to devote an hour of
your evening to watching TV. You will find that
you can relax most comfortably - sitting/lying down.   sitting

Choose a couch or a comfortable chair. Don't
perch precariously on a supposedly decorative
modern chair or on some flimsy period piece.

If you are very fortunate, you will have a
platform rocker, a recliner, or some similar
chair, which has a back high enough to support
your head and neck.

If you find yourself seated on a couch which is
placed against one of the walls of the room, put
one or more pillows against the wall behind your
head.

If you have to sit on an ordinary easy chair or
on a couch which is not placed against the wall,
slide down to a point where your head is supported
by the back of the couch or chair. Your final
position - will/will not - be as comfortable as it   will not
would be in a high-backed chair, but this is the
only way for you to relax your neck muscles, a
principal source of tension when you sit down.

In terms of remaining relaxed while sitting,
decide whether each of the following statements
is true or false:

1. You should avoid flimsy chairs with hard
   seats and backs.   true

2. You should avoid couches and easy chairs.   false

3. You should look for comfortable chairs with
   backs which are higher than your head.   true

4. You should always try to see that your head
   is well supported.   true

5. You should always sit with your weight well
   forward and your back absolutely straight.   false

If you are sitting in an easy chair with arms,
spread your elbows well out so that your own
arms are lying comfortably along the arms
of the chair.

Should most of the weight of your arms be
supported by your shoulders?   no

If you are sitting on a couch or an armless
chair, let your hands rest comfortably in your
lap and let your arms lie in against your body
so that most of their weight is supported by
your chest and stomach.

As you might guess, you can relax more
comfortably in an easy chair - with/without -   with
arms.

You should now be sitting back in a position
which is very comfortable for your head, trunk
and arms, but which still leaves considerable
tension in your legs and feet.

If you are not already wearing slippers, remove
your shoes; put your feet up on a foot stool, on a
hassock, or even on another chair. You will
immediately feel the release of tension in your
legs and feet.

Remember that you have a <u>right</u> to be comfortable
at all times. Your primary objective should be

  1. maintaining your own comfort and
      well-being.

  2. conforming to other people's conventions.   1

Still in terms of remaining relaxed, answer
the following questions:

1. Should men always keep their coats on,
    their collars buttoned, and their ties
    tight?   no

2. Should women wear high-heeled shoes
    two sizes too small?   no

3. Should either sex wear uncomfortable
    clothes simply because they are "in
    style"?   no

Incidentally, this advice extends to the working
situation. If you insist on the tight and
unbelievably uncomfortable clothing that many
people wear to work, you will find that you are
less comfortable and less efficient than you
might otherwise be. Such clothes defeat their
purpose. They are designed to look attractive,
but they make you - more/less - awkward and   more
self-conscious than your comfortably dressed
colleagues.

Give the five techniques of general relaxation   smiling
which are appropriate for a TV viewer.   yawning
                                                    stretching
                                                    deep breathing
                                                    repetition of the
                                                    word relax

What is the only technique which seems   closing
inappropriate for a person watching TV?   your eyes

And even this technique can be used very effectively during commercials and uninteresting
sequences. You will find that it helps you to
avoid headaches.

Remember that the TV set is there for your
amusement. There is no law which says that
you have to keep your eyes glued to the screen.
Station breaks offer an excellent chance to
practice progressive relaxation.

Many people say that they relax in the evening
by watching TV thrillers. Such shows induce
more muscular tension than many working
situations. They offer distraction, but they
won't afford _____ to persons who   relaxation
haven't learned how to release their muscular
tensions.

Television viewers would live longer and enjoy
themselves more if they knew how to avoid tying
themselves in knots. Certain minimal muscular
tensions accompany the sitting position, but the
only muscles which are really used in watching
the programs are those of the _____.   eyes

Even the eye muscles should be

1.   as tense as possible.

2.   as relaxed as they can be, while still
     permitting you to follow the program.   2

Blink your eyes often when watching TV. It not
only relaxes them briefly but also moistens the
eyeballs.

Blinking your eyes frequently and closing them
during commercials and station breaks will help
you to avoid eye strain and will also contribute to
the general _____ of your entire body.   relaxation

SITTING AND DOING NOTHING

Many situations in modern life require us to sit
and do nothing. Among examples which come to
mind immediately are the following:

(1)   riding in cars, busses, trains, or planes

(2)   waiting for plays, movies, or concerts to
      begin.

(3)   waiting to be served in restaurants

(4)   having a haircut, facial, manicure, or
      permanent wave

(5) sitting in waiting rooms at airports, train stations, bus stations, etc.

(6) sitting in the outer offices of dentists, doctors, lawyers, etc.

These are excellent opportunties to use the
techniques of general relaxation or to
practice _____ relaxation.   progressive

When you find yourself in such a waiting
situation, approximate the relaxed position
recommended for viewing TV. You will
have the additional advantage of being able
to close your eyes.

Obviously your physical and social environment
will sometimes prevent you from loosening your
collar, removing your shoes, putting your feet up,
etc; but you <u>can</u> achieve a state of comfortable
relaxation which will allow you to recuperate
during situations which could otherwise constitute
annoyances.

READING

Some people prefer to carry a book and read
during waiting situations. Again, they should
try to approximate as closely as possible the
position used for watching TV.

Can your eyes be completely relaxed when
you are watching TV?   no

When you read a book, do you have to tense
your eyes somewhat, and move them to
follow the print?   yes

Would you suspect that it would be a good
idea to blink frequently?   yes

Might it also be worthwhile to close your
eyes occasionally for extended periods of
time?

yes

Thus there are great similarities between
reading a book and watching _____.

television (TV)

There is one principal difference. Little
deliberate muscular exertion is required
of a TV viewer. He - holds/does not hold -
the set in his hand.

does not hold

Does he watch the screen with his arms or
legs?

no

But a person reading a book ordinarily holds
it in one or both hands. He is also required to
turn pages. A certain amount of _____
muscular tension exists in at least one arm
and hand.

specific

The point to remember is that the specific
tension in the eye muscles and in the arm
and hand muscles involved in reading should
be the absolute - minimum/maximum -
needed to hold the book in position, turn the
pages, and follow the meaning.

minimum

If you continually shift your position while
you read, you are still uncomfortably tense.
Close your book for a moment and practice
progressive relaxation.

RELAXING WHILE WORKING AT A DESK

Many people in our society have office jobs.
Others spend considerable time at home doing
such desk work as writing letters, checking
accounts, planning budgets, making out
shopping lists, etc.

If you are writing with a pen or a pencil, do
you have any reason to tense the muscles of
your legs and feet?   no

Assuming that you are right handed, must your
left hand be tense?   no

While writing at a desk, you will maintain the
minimum necessary amount of _____   specific
tension in your eye, neck and back muscles,
and in the muscles of your right arm and hand.
Decide whether each of the following is a sign
of tension or relaxation in a person who is
writing:

1.	He suffers continually from writer's cramp.	tension
2.	He gnaws at his lower lip.	tension
3.	He drums on the desk top.	tension
4.	His left arm lies motionless.	relaxation
5.	He bites his pencil.	tension
6.	He complains of a neckache.	tension
7.	He scowls as he works.	tension
8.	Only the hand with the pencil seems to move.	relaxation
9.	His body seems absolutely rigid.	tension
10.	He smiles as he works.	relaxation
11.	His face has a worried expression.	tension
12.	He continually twists his pencil in his fingers.	tension
13.	He writes steadily with few pauses for revision.	relaxation

RELAXED DRIVING

Driving is both safer and more enjoyable
when you are relaxed. But driving a car
necessarily involves - more/less - muscular   more
tension than watching TV or reading a book.

Again our objective will be to introduce only
the absolute _____ of specific tension   minimum
necessary to drive effectively.

Generalizing from your previous experience
with relaxation in the sitting position, decide
whether the following statements about driving
are true or false:

1. You should practice your techniques of
   relaxation before starting the car.   true

2. You should sit hunched forward in the
   driver's seat.   false

3. Your back should rest against the back
   of the front seat.   true

4. If you don't need your left foot in driving,
   it should remain comfortably at rest.   true

5. You should hold the wheel as tightly as
   possible.   false

6. Your right leg should be only tense
   enough to work the accelerator and
   the brake.   true

7. The more tense you are, the more
   rapidly you will become tired of
   driving.   true

8. Keeping yourself tense is a good way
   to avoid becoming tired when driving.   false

9. Tense, nervous drivers are less likely
   to have accidents.   false

10. It is easier to concentrate on your
    driving when you are relaxed.   true

11. Red lights offer a good opportunity to
    stretch and close your eyes.   true

12. Your driving will be safer and more enjoyable if you keep a smile on your face.   true

13. It is helpful to worry about the mechanical condition of your car.   false

14. You should maintain a strict driving schedule which permits you only a minimum of time to reach your destination.   false

15. You should always start early and give yourself plenty of time.   true

16. Any sign of weariness is an indication that you should park your car and rest.   true

17. Fast driving is usually good driving.   false

18. You should keep your eyes "glued to the road."   false

19. You should blink often and allow your eyes to move from side to side of the road.   true

20. Driving offers you a good chance to get rid of hostility.   false

21. If you succeed in remaining relaxed, you won't have any hostility to get rid of.   true

Is the driver of a car in a variation of the basic sitting position?   yes

Some of a driver's muscles must be specifically tensed. Should he nevertheless try to approximate a state of general relaxation?   yes

There will be enough tension in his _____ muscles to allow him to watch the road.   eye

His _____ muscles will be sufficiently tensed to hold his head up.   neck

Both hands will be sufficiently tensed to hold the wheel in a firm but - light/heavy - grasp.   light

His arm muscles will be tensed sufficiently
to hold up the small portion of their weight
which is not supported by the wheel.   His
_____ leg will be tense enough to allow   right
his foot to control the accelerator and the
brake.

A driver who practices the appropriate
techniques of relaxation will eventually
eliminate muscular _____ from the   tension
rest of his body.

A relaxed driver is confident and comfortable.
He is not a hostile threat to the safety of other
motorists.

RELAXING AT MEALTIME

Competitive attitudes are out of place at work.
They seem even less suitable at the dinner
table.   Many Americans eat as if they were
involved in a race.   Since there is usually
plenty to eat for all concerned, this behavior
seems - appropriate/inappropriate.   inappropriate

Should eating be looked upon as a disagreeable
task to be finished as rapidly as possible?   no

Should mealtimes be set aside as periods
devoted to relaxation and the slow enjoyment
of food?   yes

A person who gulps his food down mechanically
and then rushes away from the table

1.   will never suffer from indigestion.

2.   is obviously benefiting psychologically
     and physically from his meals.

3.   shows little concern for his own physical
     well-being.

4.   will necessarily be more successful in
     business than a slow eater.   3

Answer true or false to the following
statements about eating:

1. You should remind yourself to relax
    before starting to eat.   true

2. You should sit down while you eat.   true
                                                        (A surprising
                                                        number of people
                                                        often eat while
                                                        standing in
                                                        cafeterias or
                                                        walking around
                                                        the house.)

3. There is no need to tense either of
    your legs.   true

4. Assuming that you are right handed,
    your left hand can remain relaxed
    much of the time.   true

5. You will digest your food better if
    you relax.   true

6. You should try to let yourself sink
    down into the chair.   true

7. Mealtime conversation should be light
    and pleasant.   true

8. You should eat as fast as possible.   false

9. During the course of a meal, you
    should pause occasionally and practice
    relaxation.   true

10. While eating, you will not find it
    necessary to tense the muscles of your
    mouth and jaw at all.   false

11. The dinner table is an excellent place
    for settling disputes.   false

12. It is important to maintain strict
    discipline at the family table.   false

13. Everyone at the table should be made
    to feel as comfortable as possible.   true

The chairs in most American dining rooms are
ridiculously uncomfortable. They seem more
like torture instruments than invitations to
relaxed dining.

You will enjoy your meals more if you sit in
an upholstered chair with arms and a high back.
Such a chair will help you to sit back comfortably
and relax before and after eating; while you eat,
it will serve as a constant reminder to settle
back from the table occasionally for moments of
relaxation.

Should you develop the habit of interrupting
your eating from time to time for a few
seconds of practice in relaxation?   yes

Do you have to finish everything on your plate
as fast as possible?   no

Should you schedule your day so that you always
have plenty of time to eat?   yes

FORGETTING THE SPECTATORS

As we have previously noted, most of modern
man's tensions - are/aren't - associated with   are
other people.

Even when they have definite tasks to perform,
many people become tense when they feel that
others are watching them. The most experienced
participants in competitive sports occasionally
feel so nervous that they perform very badly.

If you find yourself becoming tense while
performing before others, remind yourself
to relax and concentrate on what you are
doing. It will often help to verbalize each
step of your task.

Thus if a crowd is watching you repair a car,
and you find yourself becoming nervous, you
might say to yourself, "The first step is taking
off the air filter. It is held on by this wing nut.
I turn the wing nut counterclockwise to loosen
it, and then remove the air filter itself, etc."
You will find that this helps you to forget the
crowd and to function calmly and efficiently.

RELAXING AT SOCIAL GATHERINGS

We have just seen how difficult it is to remain
relaxed while people watch you work. Relaxation
becomes even more difficult when people are
staring at you and you are required to remain
still. You then have the problem of deciding
what to do with your arms and legs.

At such times most people tend to assume
awkward, rigid positions. They seem barely
able to breathe because of the tension in their
chest muscles. They shift their arms and
legs frequently in attempts to find comfortable
positions because tension makes their muscles
ache.

As we have noticed previously, tension and
relaxation are - compatible/incompatible.   incompatible

A social gathering at which you are required
simply to sit is an excellent opportunity for you
to practice several aids to general relaxation.
Some of the others will be inappropriate. Will
you yawn continually?   no

Will you stretch often?   no

Will you close your eyes for long periods of
time?   no

Might you try letting just the suggestion of
a smile play about your lips?   yes

Will it do any harm to remind yourself to
breathe deeply?   no

Will you be able to repeat the word <u>relax</u> to
yourself?   yes

In such a situation, remember to practice
progressive relaxation over and over again.
Tell yourself to relax your feet, your lower
legs, your upper legs, etc. After you have
thus relaxed all the muscle groups in your
body, repeat the entire process. Remember
that you - can/cannot - be relaxed and tense   cannot
at the same time.

While you are relaxing, you will have no
opportunity to feel self-conscious. Remember
that your own enjoyment is your primary objective.
In order to enjoy yourself, you must remain
_____.   relaxed

Incidentally, a secondary result of your relaxed
attitude will be an increased ability to enjoy the
company of other people. You will be better able
to follow the conversation and to participate
appropriately. Your relaxation will communicate
itself to others, and you will find that, while
enjoying yourself, you will have made a favorable
impression on the other members of the group.

Should making a favorable impression on others
be as important to you as your own enjoyment?   no

Should enjoying yourself be your main objective?   yes

Any time that you worry about the impression
you are making on other people, you are assuming
that control of your happiness resides

1. inside of you.

2. inside of them.   2

Remember to remain in control of your own
reactions. If you let your life be manipulated
by other people, you will resemble a puppet
whose limbs are jerked about by invisible strings.

RELAXING WHILE STANDING

Our first basic position was _____ _____.   lying down

Our second basic position was _____.   sitting

Standing is the third basic position. From the
point of view of relaxation, the first thing to
remember about standing is this: Stand only
when you have to.

Take to heart this well-known advice which
has been attributed to many sources: "Never
stand when you can sit; never sit when you can
lie down; never remain awake when you can
sleep."

This counsel may be somewhat exaggerated,
but many Americans would live longer and
happier lives if they reminded themselves of
it occasionally.

In any event, don't stand on aching legs and
feet when it is just as easy to sit down. It is
only relatively recently, in evolutionary terms,
that man has spent so much time on his feet.
Universal complaints of back trouble indicate
that the decision to walk erect may have been
something of a mistake.

When conversing, working, speaking to a
group, or just waiting for something to
happen, - stand/sit - whenever possible.   sit

Remember that you have a right to sit down
if it doesn't interfere with your work. Many
machine operators suffer through jobs which
could be pleasant, because they feel that they
have to remain in a standing position. Their
feet swell, their arches flatten, their legs and
bent back ache--all because they won't sit down.
Even if the work area is at what is ordinarily
considered to be standing height, special tall
chairs may be used. Is a relaxed and
comfortable worker less likely to have an
accident?   yes

HOUSEWORK

The housewife has one of the most difficult
jobs in our society. We all know stories of
brawny males who collapsed after trying to
follow their wives through a day of housework.

Too many women drive themselves to the point
of exhaustion. They would be not only happier
but also more efficient if they devoted more
time to rest and relaxation.

The cardinal rule for housewives is similar
to that for machine operators. Never stand
to perform any task when it is possible to
_____.   sit

Buy several chairs the height of a tall kitchen
stool. Place them at convenient spots around
the house. Don't stand while you iron or
prepare meals. Considerable polishing and
dusting can also be done from a sitting position.

Even soldiers on a march are allowed five
minutes of rest an hour. When engaged in
heavy housework, should you lie down for
five minutes at the end of each hour?   yes

Is this rest period a good time to practice
the techniques of relaxation?   yes

Although her job is hard, the housewife is
in a very advantageous position if she will
only realize it. Since she has a right to
decide how and when she will perform each
task, she can set up her own schedule. Does   Only if she
she have a tense, hard-driving boss watching   plays this role
her every move?   herself.

In this respect she is - more/less - fortunate   more
than most American males.

In terms of relaxation, the housewife has
another advantage over her husband. Since
her place of work is her own house, she
- is/isn't - permitted to place reminders to   is
relax wherever she pleases.

Many of the housewife's problems are her
own making. She is often compulsive and
overly conscientious. She sacrifices her
comfort and that of her family to an ideal
picture of how her home should look. She
forgets that a home is useful only so far as

1. it looks like something out of a
   women's magazine.

2. it impresses her neighbors.

3. it is kept absolutely shining.

4. it contributes to the happiness
   of the people who live in it.   4

Can you suggest some techniques of general
relaxation which the housewife might practice
as she works?

smiling
yawning
stretching
closing her eyes
deep breathing
repetition of
the word <u>relax</u>

Is the housewife in a better position to
practice yawning and stretching than most
other people in our society?

yes

If you are a woman who does considerable
housework, don't demand too much of yourself.
Your goal should be your own enjoyment, not
the accomplishment of an impossible amount of
work. You are in an excellent position to control
your own happiness. Don't subordinate yourself
to a series of unnecessary rules. Remember
that the more relaxed and happy you are, the
- more/less - happiness you can communicate
to your family.

more

STANDING AND TALKING

Whenever you find yourself standing and talking
to friends for a long period of time, remember
that they are as uncomfortable as you are. Take
command of the situation. They will welcome
your suggestion that everyone sit down.

Of course there are situations in which there is
no way out of it. You just have to stand. You
can prepare for these situations by practicing
relaxation in the standing position. Try the
following:

First approximate general relaxation as closely
as possible. Stand with your feet about ten inches
apart and your toes pointed slightly outward. If
your feet are much farther apart, your position
becomes strained and awkward. If they are closer
together, you have to tense muscles first in one
leg and then in the other in order to maintain your
balance.

Relax your legs as much as possible. A
number of muscle groups will still remain
quite _____ because they have to perform   tense
work in order to hold you up.

Now relax the muscles of your lower back,
upper back, shoulders and arms. Let your
arms hang limply and heavily. Feel them
pull downward from your limp shoulders.
Breathe slowly and deeply, with a feeling
of release in your chest muscles each time
you exhale.

Relax the muscles of your scalp, forehead,
jaw, mouth and tongue. Does your jaw sag
downward when relaxed?   yes

Does your tongue seem to float in your mouth?   It should.

When you are first learning how to relax,
practice standing in the position several
times a day. Obviously you - can/can't -   can't
let your jaw sag and your tongue float when
you are talking to someone.

But you should remind yourself of this relaxed
position whenever you do have to stand and talk.
Specific tensions will creep in, but you will still
be able to approximate _____ relaxation   general
quite closely.

You will find this practice useful in public
speaking, singing or acting. Speech teachers
spend an enormous amount of time teaching
their students to relax the muscles of the throat
and the respiratory organs. If you are in a
state of general relaxation, will these muscles
necessarily be relaxed?   yes

Is a shrill metallic tone in a speaker's voice
an indication of tension?   yes

Proper relaxation will help to give you a
low, pleasant voice with good carrying power.
A _____ person can speak for long   relaxed
periods of time without tiring or losing his
voice.

Does a relaxed singer or actor convey an
attractive impression of ease and control?   yes

The impression which a relaxed performer
communicates is actually

1. more important than the fact that he
    is enjoying himself.

2. less important than the fact that he
    is enjoying himself.

3. completely unimportant.   2

SUMMARY

Give the three basic positions in which we   lying down
have practiced relaxation.   sitting
                                                           standing

In which position can you relax most
completely?   lying down

Rank the three basic positions in order from   1. standing
least restful to most restful.   2. sitting
                                                           3. lying down

A person standing will find it

1. easier to relax than when he is
    sitting.

2. impossible to relax at all.

3. possible to relax somewhat in spite of
    considerable necessary specific tension.   3

When you are standing, it is easier to relax

1. with your weight balanced evenly
    between your feet.

2. with all your weight on one foot.

3. by shifting your weight from one
    foot to the other.   1

Is relaxation a help in public speaking?   yes

As you become more relaxed, the tone of
your voice tends to become - higher/lower.   lower

You can speak for much longer periods of
time when you are - tense/relaxed.   relaxed

A speaker should think first of

1. how relaxed he is.

2. how relaxed his audience is.

3. what sort of impression he is making.   1

One result of a speaker's relaxed attitude will
be a - favorable/unfavorable - impression on   favorable
his audience.

RELAXATION WHILE WALKING

We have already seen that relaxed people tend
to give a - hurried/leisurely - impression.   leisurely

People who are always in a rush seem pompous,
ridiculous, and somehow mechanical.   It is
obvious that they think that happiness is external
and that they are chasing it (or running from it).
To us they seem as silly as people who drive or
eat as if they were in a race.

A relaxed person makes it obvious that his
emotional control is - inside/outside.   inside

In terms of remaining relaxed, decide whether the following statements about walking are true or false:

1. Walking is an exercise which can be practiced even by very old men and women.   true

2. In order to get the most out of walking, you should tense all your muscles with each step.   false

3. As you walk, your entire body should feel loose and free.   true

4. Your body should be held rigidly erect.   false

5. Your arms should be held close against your sides.   false

6. In walking you should hunch forward as much as possible.   false

7. You should allow your arms to swing gently with the natural movement of your body.   true

8. You will feel the greatest amount of specific tension in your leg muscles.   true

9. You should tense your leg muscles as much as possible.   false

10. No matter how tired you are, you should force yourself to take a daily walk.   false

11. You will ordinarily be more relaxed if you walk with a smile on your face.   true

12. People who scowl and scurry rapidly along the city streets give an impression of importance and self-control.   false

13. You can practice relaxing your arms and shoulders while walking.   true

14. It is good to remind yourself that you have every right to stop and sit down frequently.   true

15. Your daily walk should become a perfectly mechanical routine.   false

16. The more relaxed you are, the more you will enjoy your walk.   true

17. An easy, relaxed walk is an indication of a happy state of mind.   true

18. Stopping occasionally to yawn and stretch will help you to remain relaxed.   true

19. You should always walk as if you are in a hurry to get somewhere.   false

SPORTS AND OTHER ACTIVITIES

Does walking constitute good exercise for
most people?   yes

Golf is a game which involves considerable
walking. Does this mean that a hard-driving,
competitive game of golf is necessarily good
for you?   no

Golf won't help you to relax if you worry about
the score. Compete with yourself and watch
your improvement, but don't transfer the
attitudes of a competitive business man to the
golf course. Incidentally, a relaxed game of
golf is quite often a better game of golf. But
you should keep in mind the fact that your
principal objective is

    1.   a better game of golf.

    2.   your own relaxed enjoyment.   2

You should remain relaxed even when swinging
at a golf ball. Does relaxation also contribute
to bowling well and to playing a good game of
tennis?   yes

Any sport demands a relaxed control of your
muscles. You will play much better and much
longer if you tense only those muscles which are
needed to perform a given task. Should they be
relaxed as soon as they are no longer needed?   yes

The secret of the relaxed poise of a dancer,
driver, or trapeze artist lies in the _____   relaxation
of muscles which are not being used. There is
a striking contrast between the extreme
relaxation of some muscles in an athlete's body
and the superbly directed use of others.

Let's generalize this observation to include
any activity, whether classified as work or
sport, by saying that the beginner indulges
in all sorts of inappropriate behavior. He
wriggles, squirms, and strikes embarrassingly
strained and awkward poses. Gradually
he learns that much of this activity fails to
contribute to his goal. Instead of tiring
himself needlessly and making himself appear
ludicrous, he remains relaxed until the very
moment when his muscles must perform work.
He then tenses

1. fewer muscles than he needs.

2. only those muscles which are
   actually being used.

3. his whole body as much as possible.   2

The athlete or worker should introduce into
the muscles which he needs to use the
- maximum/minimum - amount of tension   minimum
required to perform the task at hand.

FINAL REVIEW

We review often in this course because
relaxation is easy to learn but hard to
remember. Observation of yourself and
others indicates why you should relax.
But to prevent tension from creeping back
into your life you must monitor your
reactions constantly. Your new relaxed
attitude goes against the accumulated
habit strength of a lifetime.

Soon you will check your progress by
taking a final examination and then
practicing what you have learned in
critical situations. For the moment,
let's review some important concepts.

From my viewpoint, everything that happens
to me occurs

    1. in the outside world.

    2. inside of me.   2

Are all my tensions inside of me?   yes

My fears and pains, joys and sorrows, are
located ....   inside of me

Are all my feelings located inside of my
body?   yes

Can I control my body to the extent of
closing its eyes, making it laugh, smile,
yawn, or think about pleasant things?   yes

Does this mean that I can be relaxed and
happy if I decide to be?   yes

Instead of saying that I laugh when I am happy,   I am happy
I might say that ....   when I laugh.

People often say that they yawn when they are
relaxed. They might also say that ....   they are relaxed
....   when they yawn.

Might we extend this argument to say that
a man has succeeded if he chooses to view
his life as a success?   yes

Success in life is

1. an objective achievement to be measured
   in terms of the number of material things
   a person can accumulate.

2. a subjective achievement which depends
   upon the opinions of others.

3. a state of mind which depends upon an
   individual's way of viewing things.   3

We decide that other people are unhappy when
we see that they have certain reactions--when
they cry, look sad, frown, and exhibit symptoms
of tension.

We say that others are happy when we see them
smile, laugh and show signs of relaxation.

Many people think that their reactions are
caused by persons or things in the outside
world. Do a person's reactions actually
come from inside of him?   yes

Once you have learned to control your reactions,
can you decide whether you are going to exhibit
symptoms of tension or relaxation, of happiness
or unhappiness?   yes

In terms of our present definition, if your
reactions are those of a relaxed, happy
person, we will consider you to be

1. fooling other people.

2. fooling yourself.

3. a relaxed, happy person.   3

If a person learning to work at a new task or
play at a new sport is preoccupied with his
audience, will he become uncomfortably tense?   yes

Are some people so terrified of being laughed
at or criticized that they are unable to bring
themselves to undertake new activities?   yes

Learning a new task or game will be incomparably
more pleasant if the beginner remembers that his
primary goal is

1. to impress his audience.

2. to enjoy himself.

3. to demonstrate his superiority over
    the game.   2

Once the beginner has relaxed, he will be able
to direct his attention and energies away from
his audience and toward his secondary goal,
the development of a new skill.

Choose the ways in which a relaxed person can
bring comfort and happiness into the lives of
his associates?

1. pointing out the grave consequences
    of their mistakes.

2. helping them to laugh at their mistakes.   2

3. contributing to their burden of guilt by
    saying constantly, "you shouldn't have"
    or "you mustn't."

4. treating every problem as a crisis.

5. refusing to tolerate any discussion
    of their problems.

6. helping them to attack problems with
    confidence in their ability to resolve
    them.   6

Public figures seem ridiculous when they
dwell upon "their public, their greatness,
their reputations, " etc. , as if greatness
and happiness were external objects to be
accumulated along with other material
possessions. We find such persons silly
because they make it obvious that they are

1.   truly great people.

2.   puppets controlled by other
     people's opinions.

3.   really happy people.   2

Many people fear the results of an unwise
purchase, or the loss of a house or job, as
if these things might mean death or starvation.
Is failure to exercise maximum control over
your environment ordinarily disastrous in our
society?   no

Does starvation represent a serious threat
to most of our populace?   no

In our society, people suffer primarily from

1.   lack of money.

2.   lack of material things

3.   their own emotional disturbances.   3

Therefore learning to be relaxed and happy
should be the - primary/secondary - goal of   primary
most Americans.

FINAL EXAM

Decide whether each of the following statements about a <u>relaxed</u> <u>person</u> is true or false. Keep track of your errors.

1.	He feels tired all the time.	false
2.	He can fall into a deep, restful sleep at will.	true
3.	He is constantly emotionally upset.	false
4.	He is greatly disturbed by minor annoyances in his environment.	false
5.	In most situations he seems to control the elements which concern him.	true
6.	He tends to over-react to insults.	false
7.	He broods constantly over his lack of worldly success.	false
8.	He doesn't worry about the justice or injustice of other people's actions toward him.	true
9.	He is constantly in fear of events which he cannot control.	false
10.	He is hypercritical of himself and other people.	false
11.	He is overly concerned with financial or material "security."	false
12.	His life is a constant round of social activities.	false
13.	He usually has time for the things he wants to do.	true
14.	He is often moody and depressed, and complains of severe headaches.	false

15. He becomes enraged over the stupidity and insensitivity of other people.   false

16. He feels that life is worthwhile.   true

17. He is often wildly excited.   false

18. He tends to smile often.   true

19. He is constantly trying to do impossible things.   false

20. His goal is to conform to the standards of his society.   false

21. He often stops what he is doing to enjoy a few moments of relaxation.   true

22. He habitually walks very fast.   false

23. He is in control of his own body.   true

24. He speaks rapidly.   false

25. His voice is low and controlled.   true

26. He closes his eyes for brief periods of time throughout the day.   true

27. He is very impatient when waiting his turn in any sort of line.   false

28. He tends to breathe slowly and deeply.   true

29. He feels that he has no right to a moment of his own.   false

30. He believes that happiness is a state of mind, rather than something to be found in the external world.   true

31. He has a tendency toward ulcers.   false

32. He thinks only of fulfilling his duty to others.   false

33. He eats slowly and savors his food.   true

34. He has a constant need for alcohol.   false

35. He enjoys walking.   true

36. He often has temper tantrums.   false

37. He takes lots of time in getting ready
for bed.   true

38. He sometimes enjoys a warm bath before
going to bed.   true

39. He has trouble waking up in the morning.   false

40. He enjoys laughing at himself and others.   true

41. He habitually speaks in a very loud voice.   false

42. He feels inadequate in most situations.   false

43. He spends much of his time thinking about
how much he hates his enemies.   false

44. He enjoys his job.   true

45. He knows that only through self-sacrifice
can he make others happy.   false

46. He feels that he has a right to enjoy
every moment of his life.   true

47. He must have the last word in any argument.   false

48. He spends long periods of time making one
difficult decision after another.   false

49. He enjoys watching television but does
not use it as an escape from daily problems.   true

50. He habitually reads himself to sleep with
a best seller.   false

51. He is self-directed.   true

52. He seldom goes to bed before three in
the morning.   false

53. He eats heavily before retiring.   false

54. He speaks only of his failures. false

55. He seems to accept and like himself. true

56. When working at a desk, he hunches
his shoulders forward and twists his
feet around the legs of his chair. false

57. He welcomes interruptions in his work
as opportunities to practice the techniques
of relaxation. true

58. He allows the words and actions of
other people to wound him deeply. false

59. He tends to drive himself hard and to
work excessively long hours. false

60. He relaxes at lunch. true

61. He finds any sort of work boring and
unstimulating. false

62. He is constantly in a state of friction
with his co-workers. false

63. He tries to get to and from work as fast as
possible. false

64. He works efficiently. true

65. He is accident prone. false

66. He shows symptoms of nervousness,
such as fidgeting and fiddling with
small objects. false

67. He is generally well liked. true

68. He is highly competitive at work and
at play. false

69. He thinks of driving as a good chance to
get rid of hostility. false

70. He views all other drivers as threats. false

71. He is very impatient when stopped
    by traffic lights.   false

72. He always drives a little over the speed
    limit, but watches closely for traffic
    policemen.   false

73. He often grinds his teeth.   false

74. If he tires while driving, he stops the
    car and rests.   true

75. He drives slumped forward across the
    wheel.   false

76. He hates all stop signals.   false

77. He complains constantly about other
    drivers' mistakes.   false

78. He blinks often and avoids staring
    fixedly at the road.   true

79. He chafes at all traffic rules and
    regulations.   false

80. He insists that his house always be
    spotless and neat.   false

81. He can't stand his children's noise and has
    made it a rule that they are to be quiet when
    he is at home.   false

82. He becomes very disturbed when something
    is out of place on his desk at work or on
    his dresser at home.   false

83. He always allows himself plenty of time
    when driving.   true

84. He hates interruptions.   false

85. He is thought of as a rational, objective
    person.   true

86. He is constantly bothered by minor aches
    and pains.   false

87. He seems to find joy in all his activities
throughout the day.   true

88. He strives constantly to improve the
manners of those around him.   false

89. He often wrinkles his forehead.   false

90. If possible, he lies down occasionally
during the day.   true

91. He is a restless sleeper.   false

92. He smokes constantly.   false

93. He is forever venting his hostility
on someone.   false

94. He is comfortable only when he is
listening to his own voice.   false

95. He seems to enjoy meeting new people.   true

96. When with large groups of people, he
is uncomfortable and often unpleasant.   false

97. He over-reacts to pain.   false

98. He seems to view life as an interesting
game.   true

99. He has constant need for the lift that
coffee, tea, and other stimulating
drinks give him.   false

100. He relaxes all the voluntary muscles
in his body except those he is actually
using.   true

101. He likes to try new things.   true

102. He finds it hard to concentrate on what
people are saying.   false

103. The emotions he formerly associated with
muscle tension have tended to disappear.   true

104. His day consists of a series of unrelated and compulsive activities. false

105. He is a perfectionist. false

106. He is constantly telling others his troubles. false

107. He appears to be comfortable and self-confident. true

108. He becomes very nervous when he is left alone with his thoughts. false

109. He fears responsibility. false

110. He often has to repress anger. false

111. He is seldom in a hurry. true

112. He is constantly showing off. false

113. He requires frequent praise from other people. false

114. He makes decisions very easily. true

115. He never admits that he has made a mistake. false

116. He stores up resentment and thinks constantly of his failures. false

117. He is always trying to "keep up with the Joneses." false

118. He makes other people feel very relaxed and comfortable when they are with him. true

119. His most important goal is to have
everyone like him.   false

120. He is generally thought of as a cheerful
person.   true

121. He likes to remain standing for long periods
of time.   false

122. He easily becomes infected with other
people's nervous tensions.   false

123. Before he does anything, he always asks
himself what his friends will think.   false

124. He engages in violent arguments on
political issues.   false

125. He usually appears well rested.   true

126. He has a servile attitude toward
authority.   false

127. He is open-minded on controversial
issues.   true

128. He often feels inferior to those about
him.   false

129. He has learned to relax when he is with
others.   true

130. He knows that money is the most important
thing in life.   /   false

131. He hates his wife.   false

132. He never stands when it's as easy to sit
down.   true

133. He frequently takes tranquilizers.   false

134. He thinks about his work day and night.   false

135. He tends to talk too much.   false

136. He sighs constantly.   false

137. He finds it easy to understand another
     person's point of view.   true

138. He spends his time lecturing others on
     their faults.   false

139. He is happy and feels that his life is a
     success.   true

140. In interpersonal situations, he keeps his
     goals clearly in mind.   true

141. He views other people's dislike of him as
     their problem.   true

142. He finds it easy to concentrate on what he
     is doing.   true

143. He often expresses self-righteous indignation.   false

144. He reacts violently to external situations
     beyond his control.   false

145. He races rapidly from one sub-goal to another.   false

146. He gets along on an absolute minimum of sleep.   false

147. He believes that happiness is found in oneself.   true

To find your score on the final examination,
subtract the number of errors you made from
100. Thus if you had 25 errors your score
is _____.   75

A BRIEF POST-GRADUATE COURSE

A high score on the final exam indicates that
you can now recognize symptoms of tension
and that you know how to eliminate them.

But, as we have emphasized frequently, it is
not enough simply to know how to relax. Your
goal is to be relaxed. Relaxation must become
a part of your pattern of living; all your reactions
must be those of a relaxed person.

With this end in view, we have given you hundreds
of opportunities to interact with this text. You
have practiced relaxation in dozens of situations.
You know the appropriate responses to all sorts
of tension-producing stimuli. You must now use
these responses in your day-by-day living.

Often your old habit patterns will tend to reassert
themselves. You must then keep clearly in mind
your goal of being a relaxed and happy person.
Train yourself to recognize signs of tension.
Remember that tension manifests itself not only
in your attitude toward others, but also in your
attitude toward _____ .   yourself

Whenever you find yourself about to react in a
tense and hostile fashion, pause for a moment
and choose the appropriate response.

If you wish to evaluate the extent to which
relaxed responses have become a part of your
normal way of life, try to play an appropriate
role in the following difficult situation.

Keep track of your errors. This post-test
will indicate just how relaxed you really are.

DRIVING FOR PLEASURE

You are a 35-year-old appliance salesman.
This Sunday you have promised to take your
wife and three children for a long pleasure
drive and a picnic.

You are helping your wife pack the lunch
basket. The children, who are looking
forward to getting started, interrupt your
preparations every five minutes to ask
when you will be ready to start. You tell
them

1. that if they keep bothering you
   there won't be any picnic.

2. that you will be ready to start in
   on them with a strap in about ten
   seconds.

3. to get out of your way.

4. that they can help you get ready
   by carrying a series of articles
   out to the car.   4

Once you have seen that your family, the
dog, and all the picnic paraphernalia have
been safely stowed in the car, you

1. leap into the driver's seat and
   pull away from the curb.

2. devote a moment to wondering
   whether you can really afford to
   take time off for a picnic.

3. worry about the condition of the car.

4. relax for a moment and put a smile
   on your face before touching the starter.

5. decide that the whole idea of a picnic
   is a silly waste of time, but that you
   owe the outing to your family.   4

In the back seat the dog is barking and the children are screaming with delight. Your wife is insisting that you could make better time if you took the superhighway. This is a good time to

1. tell them all to shut up.

2. laugh at them and remind yourself to remain relaxed.

3. head for the superhighway at top speed.

4. tell them that you're going to take them straight back home.   2

You continue at a comfortable rate of speed along a pleasant country road. A lone driver in a fast-moving sports car overtakes you and honks his horn impatiently. Looking in the rear view mirror, you can see him signaling for you to pull over and let him pass. You decide to

1. shake your fist out the window at him.

2. continue at your present speed while looking for a convenient place to pull over and let him pass.

3. speed up sufficiently to avoid delaying him.

4. drive down the middle of the road to prevent him from passing.

5. show him what the old bus can really do.

6. yell that if he knew how to drive he would simply pass you.

7. complain about him loudly to your family.   2

You finally find a spot where you can pull
over enough to let the sports car pass.
The driver pulls up beside you and yells,
"If you want to park that heap of yours,
don't do it in the middle of the road."
This causes you to

1. reply that if he doesn't shut up,
   you'll cheerfully park your fist
   in his face.

2. try to pull out in front of him again.

3. apologize profusely.

4. wave him past so that you can
   continue your trip.

5. cut over toward him as if you are
   going to run him down.   4

The sports car disappears in the distance,
and for a while your car is alone on the
road. Then, as you round a curve, you
meet a group of teenagers in a convertible.
Seeing that they are dangerously far over
on your side of the road, you

1. honk your horn and hold your ground
   to show that you are not to be bluffed.

2. yell threats at them.

3. scare them by pointing your car at
   them.

4. pull out of their way on the right side
   of the road.   4

After the convertible has careened past, you

1. remind yourself to relax and enjoy
   the drive.

2. turn your car around and pursue the
   convertible to give its occupants a
   lecture on safe driving.

3. continue on your way, complaining
   to your wife that the driver looked
   too young to have a license, that
   teenagers are all hoodlums, nowadays,
   etc.

4. give your children a lecture on
   irresponsibility.   1

A farmer in an ancient truck appears on the
road ahead of you. He is averaging about 20
miles an hour, and swaying from one side of
the pavement to the other. You toot your
horn, but he pays no attention. Your most
appropriate reaction is to

1. nudge him with your front bumper.

2. try to slip by him, even if you have
   to pass him on the right.

3. lean on the horn to force him to pay
   attention to you.

4. stay well back from him and enjoy the
   scenery, while waiting for him to turn off.   4

While you are dawdling along behind the truck,
a large new car whips by you and cuts in so
sharply that you have to brake suddenly to
avoid hitting it. Your reaction is to

1. honk your horn and yell at the other driver.

2. make sure that no one in your car has been
   hurt.

3. complain of the other driver's idiocy to
   your wife and children.

4. overtake the other driver and run him
   off the road.   2

In what seems to be a park area, you find
a convenient picnic spot and spread out
your lunch.   An irate gentleman arrives
and complains that you are trespassing on
his property.   In reply you tell him

1. that you are going to stay where
    you are until he proves his ownership.

2. that you don't care whether it is his
    property or not.

3. that you made an honest mistake and
    you would be grateful if he would let
    you finish the picnic.

4. that he'd better leave before he gets
    hurt.

5. that you'll get off his property just
    as fast as you can.   3

The gentleman says you can stay, but that
you are not to leave any trash behind you.
You answer

1. that he need not worry--you are a
    retired garbage collector.

2. that you think a bit of your trash would
    enhance the value of his property.

3. that he had better not insult you by
    intimating that you are a slob.

4. that you won't leave any trash.   4

As you finish packing the car for the return
trip, you discover that you have a flat tire.
The children are tired and quarrelsome; your
wife is complaining that she doesn't think she
can stand much more.   In this situation you

1. ask her how much she thinks you can
    stand.

2. spank the children.

3. change the tire.

4. walk away from the whole idiotic
    mess.   3

After changing the tire, you start back along
the route by which you came. Sunday afternoon
traffic is very heavy. You find yourself in a
line of cars.

A child runs across the road. The driver
ahead of you brakes suddenly. You stop
inches short of his rear bumper, but the
driver of the car behind you is less attentive;
he bumps the rear of your car. You get out
of the car and go back to

1. call the other driver an idiot.

2. ask to see his driver's license.

3. tell him you are going to call a
    policeman.

4. ask him if he was trying to kill you
    and your family.

5. see whether any damage was done.   5

The other driver is very apologetic, and it
turns out that he has simply bounced off your
bumper without damaging either car. You
tell him

1. that he had better pay more attention
    to his driving.

2. that you are glad that there is no
    damage and that no one has been
    hurt.

3. that you are going to report him to
    the police for reckless driving.   2

As you continue on your way, you talk to
your wife about

1. how pleasant it is to drive on a
    beautiful Sunday afternoon.

2. the minor accident which you have just had.

3. how difficult it is to travel with children.

4. the crazy drivers you find on the road
    these days.   1

Still about 15 miles from home, you stop
for gas. Although your windshield is
covered with insects, the attendant makes
no move to wipe it off. At this point you

1. ask him whether he has ever seen
   the ads on television in which his
   company guarantees splendid service.

2. tell him to wipe off the windshield and
   be quick about it.

3. ask him if he would mind wiping off
   the windshield.

4. get out and wipe off the windshield
   yourself.   3

The whole family is tired when you arrive
home. As you direct the unloading of the
car, you

1. join in the general complaining.

2. talk of what a wonderful day you
   have had.

3. think of the annoyances you encountered
   on your drive.

4. say you will never take another Sunday
   trip.

5. tell them that this is their last picnic.   2

After you have unloaded the car, you

1. rush to your desk to check over some
   accounts.

2. help your wife to begin preparing
   dinner immediately.

3. suggest that everyone rest and relax
   for a few minutes.   3

This completes the post-test entitled DRIVING
FOR PLEASURE. Use the following table to
find your score:

0 errors:	Doctor of Relaxation
1 error:	Master of Relaxation
2 errors:	Bachelor of Relaxation
3 errors:	Preparing for graduation
4 errors:	Entering your junior year
5 or more errors:	Review PROGRESSIVE RELAXATION

More seriously, if you have managed to
survive the pitfalls of your Sunday drive
without responding in a tense and hostile
way, you have benefited greatly from this
programmed course. Keep in mind the
goal of enjoying yourself, continue to
practice your techniques of relaxation,
and remember that your happiness lies

1. in owning the biggest house in town.

2. in the good opinions of others.

3. in working as hard as you can to
    achieve success.

4. in relaxed control of your own
    reactions.   4